9-12

**FUNDAMENTALS
OF
BOTANY
SERIES**

NONVASCULAR

PLANTS: FORM

AND FUNCTION

FUNDAMENTALS
OF
BOTANY
SERIES

edited by
WILLIAM A. JENSEN,
University of California
LEROY G. KAVALJIAN,
Sacramento State College

William T. Doyle

NORTHWESTERN UNIVERSITY

NONVASCULAR
PLANTS: FORM
AND FUNCTION

WADSWORTH PUBLISHING COMPANY, INC.
Belmont, California

L.C. Cat. Card No.: 64-23905

Printed in the United States of America

FOREWORD

Because of the immensity and complexity of the field of botany, the great diversity of plants, and the many methods of plant study, the problem of how to present to the student the highlights of botanical knowledge gained over centuries is not easy to solve. The authors and editors of the volumes in this series believe that an understanding of plants—their parts, their activities, and their relationship to man—is of fundamental importance in appreciating the significance of life. To stress this concept, the form and function of plants, tissues, and cells are treated together. At all levels of organization, in each volume, information gathered by morphologists, physiologists, cytologists, taxonomists, geneticists, biochemists, and ecologists is combined.

Thus, in the volume on *The Plant Cell* by William A. Jensen, the structure and function of the various cell parts are discussed together —for example, mitochondria and respiration, photosynthesis and chloroplasts. The volume by Stanton A. Cook, *Reproduction, Heredity, and Sexuality,* combines the principles of genetics with the means of reproduction in the various plant groups. *Nonvascular Plants: Form and Function,* by William T. Doyle, and *Vascular Plants: Form and Function,* by Frank B. Salisbury and Robert V. Parke, cover the major plant groups and discuss the plants in terms of morphology, physiology, and biochemistry. The relation of plants, particularly vascular plants, to their environment and to each other is covered in *Plants and the Ecosystem* by W. D. Billings. The form and distribution of plants of the past and their relation to the concepts of evolution are considered by Harlan Banks in *Evolution and Plants of the Past.* Herbert G. Baker, in *Plants and Civilization,* discusses the importance of plants to man's social and economic development and the equally important consideration of man's role in the modification and distribution of plants.

In a series such as this, the editors are faced with the task of dividing a broad field into areas that can be presented in a meaningful way by the authors. There must be logic in the entire scheme, with few gaps and a minimum of overlap. Yet an instructor may not want to use the series of volumes in the sequence and manner preferred by the editors. Consequently, each volume must be usable alone and also in any sequence with the others. To achieve such a high degree of versatility is difficult, but we believe the series exhibits these features.

A concerted effort has been made by the authors and editors to maintain a consistent level of presentation. However, each author has been encouraged to approach his subject in his own way and to write in his own style in order to provide variety and to exploit the uniqueness of the individual author's viewpoint. Finally, while presenting the principles of botany we have tried to communicate the excitement of recent developments as well as the joy that comes with the extension of knowledge in any field.

Nonvascular plants, the subject of this volume, form an extremely large and heterogeneous group. The impressive diversity in form and function at both the cellular and organismal level has made these organisms invaluable in research. Their utility as research tools has contributed to the rapid advancement of knowledge in such areas as molecular biology, cell physiology, photosynthesis, biochemical genetics, and sexual and genetic mechanisms. In addition, some are the bases of food chains in bodies of water; some have industrial uses; and some are important plant and animal parasites. Nonvascular plants have representatives in each of the major divisions of plants. This diversity in form and function is presented here in an evolutionary framework. Organisms of current research interest within each evolutionary group are discussed in detail whenever possible. Every effort has been made to indicate the dynamic nature of research on nonvascular plants. The need for further research at all levels, whether molecular or ecological, descriptive or experimental, is emphasized.

CONTENTS

1

INTRODUCTION

Nonvascular plants are a heterogeneous group including bacteria, fungi, algae, and bryophytes. They are separated from vascular plants by one distinctive feature: the lack of a lignified water-conducting tissue known as vascular tissue. Thus nonvascular plants (like the invertebrates of the animal kingdom) are defined by negation, a conceptually unsatisfactory but occasionally useful procedure.

Nonvascular plants are found in all environments capable of supporting life. They are in soil, water, and air, and they grow in desert and arctic regions as well as in cold mountain areas and hot springs. They have their most luxuriant development in tropical and subtropical regions where humidity is relatively high. Although nonvascular plants are widely distributed as a group, tolerances of individual species are usually much more restricted. For example, a species of alga growing in hot springs will usually be found only in that type of habitat. Other algae may be found only on snow.

The diversity in the form of nonvascular plants is as great as that of their distribution. Many are unicellular and microscopic. Unicellular species exhibit great morphological diversity resulting from adaptations to their particular environment. Unbranched and branched chains of cells, called *filaments,* are also common body forms. The most highly differentiated nonvascular plants possess leaflike, stemlike, and rootlike structures. One such species, a giant seaweed, may grow to a length of over 60 meters—longer than most vascular plants.

RELATIONSHIP OF FORM TO FUNCTION

It is impossible to divorce biological form from function, because form is the physical expression of function. Multicellularity in plants leads to the division of labor among component cells—in other words, to cell specialization for a specific function. Thus a multicellular moss

1

is differentiated into leaflike, stemlike, and rootlike portions. Component cells of the moss plant may be specialized for photosynthesis, water conduction, water absorption, food storage, or strengthening. Some cells are even dead in their functional state. Concomitant with specialization in cellular function is specialization in cellular form. Unicellular organisms are simple in form and structure only; they are functionally as complex as multicellular organisms. Each free-living unicell is capable of the vital functions characteristic of multicellular plants—growth, metabolism, and reproduction. Since long-term survival of species depends primarily on comparative success in reproduction (asexual or sexual) it is not surprising to find that reproductive structures of many nonvascular plants are highly specialized and adapted to particular environmental conditions.

CLASSIFICATION

There are approximately 400,000 known nonvascular and vascular plants. Evolution explains the tremendous diversity of plant types. Organisms can, and have, changed with time. Evolution also means that organisms living today were derived from pre-existing organisms. Thus evolution not only explains diversities, it also explains similarities between organisms. Knowing both the diversities and the similarities provides the necessary elements for a classification based on evolution—that is, a *phylogenetic* system. Phylogeny is the historical development of groups of individuals, or descent by change. In such a system, diversity is considered to be the result of phylogenetic change, and organisms are classified according to their evolutionary relationships. The primary trend of phylogeny has been from simple organisms to more complex ones. (Simplification has also occurred, however, especially in parasites.)

What characteristics can be used to distinguish major groups of related plants? Before an answer is attempted, a few explanatory remarks are needed. Evolution explains the origin of plant diversity. On the other hand, man becomes aware of this diversity through the study of *individual* organisms, and he records his observations in the form of data. In general, data obtained in the past are still valid today, and will remain valid in the future. For example, organisms of a particular species of alga that had two flagella 50 years ago will also have two flagella when investigated today or 50 years from now. This type of datum can be obtained again and again, and does not change. Phylogenetic conclusions derived from data, on the other hand, may change.

Organismal classification, especially at the higher-category levels, is one of the most abstract, philosophical, and mentally stimulating areas of biology. All classification schemes are based (1) on the amount and type of data available and (2) on how these data are evaluated. Investigators often interpret the same data differently—hence the existence of many different classification schemes. The classification system used in this book is but one way in which the data can be interpreted. It purports to reflect modern botanical thought on plant classification. It will most certainly undergo change in the future as additional information becomes available.

Now that you are aware of some of the problems involved in the erection of a classification system, we can return to the question at hand: What characteristics can be used to distinguish major groups of related plants? Except for reproductive structures—that is, unicellular reproductive structures in bacteria, fungi, and most algae, as opposed to multicellular reproductive structures in bryophytes and vascular plants—the general form of the plant body is not especially helpful at this level of classification.

Of prime importance are characteristics derived at the cellular level of organization, including data obtained from comparative biochemical studies. Although several kinds of data can be used, only three will be discussed.

Pigmentation. Many plants are photosynthetic In order for light energy to be trapped and made available for photosynthesis, pigment molecules must be present. It is known that pigment molecules involved in photosynthesis are not the same in all plants. For example, several kinds of chlorophyll molecules are known; at least two kinds occur in bacteria, and three or four in other plants. No organism has more than two kinds of chlorophyll molecules, some have only one, and others have none. In addition, several accessory pigments may be involved in the photosynthetic process. The distribution of pigments involved in photosynthesis is used as a clue to delimit the major groups of related plants.

Food Reserve. Food that is not immediately needed for growth is commonly stored as proteins, lipids, or carbohydrates. Several different types of carbohydrate food reserves have been identified in plants. True starch (stains blue when an iodine solution is added) is one type. The different polysaccharide food reserves, including true starch, possess glucose as the basic structural unit. The existence of different polysaccharides constructed from similar building blocks indicates the presence of different enzymatic pathways. Conversely, organisms with a similar polysaccharide food reserve most likely possess similar pathways. The type of food reserve, then, is an additional criterion useful in identifying related plants.

Flagellation. Many plants either are flagellated in the adult state or have flagellated reproductive cells. A study of a wide variety of plants shows that structure, form, number, and place of insertion of flagella are important for distinguishing species.

Flagella have two basic structures. One type, found only in bacteria, consists of a single major fibril in cross section (Fig. 1-1a). In a cross

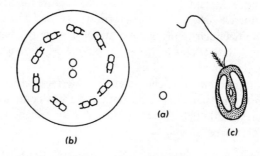

Fig. 1-1. (a) *Cross section of a bacterial flagellum showing a single fibril.* (b) *Cross section of a flagellum with a 9 + 2 arrangement of fibrils. (Note that the bacterial flagellum is of the same approximate size in section as a single central fibril of a 9 + 2 flagellum.)* (c) *Flagellated cell with a tinsel flagellum (left) and a whiplash flagellum (right).*

section of the other flagellar type there are nine peripheral and two central major fibrils (Fig. 1-1b). Each of the nine peripheral fibrils in turn consists of two subfibrils. This so-called 9 + 2 flagellar structure is characteristic of all plant flagella, other than bacteria, and of animal flagella and cilia.

Flagella of the 9 + 2 type have two common forms: whiplash and tinsel (Fig. 1-1c). Whiplash flagella are devoid of lateral structures, whereas tinsel flagella have them. In both structural types, flagella (which vary from one to many) usually are anteriorly, posteriorly, or laterally inserted.

By the evaluation and consistent application of the three kinds of data discussed above, it is possible to distinguish several large groups of plants. With the exceptions to be pointed out in the text, plants within each group are more closely related to each other than they are to plants in other groups. The classification scheme used in this book is as follows:

PLANT KINGDOM

Scientific Name	Common Name
Division Schizophyta	bacteria
Division Eumycota	fungi
Division Myxomycota	slime molds
Division Cyanophyta	blue-green algae
Division Rhodophyta	red algae
Division Chrysophyta	golden algae and diatoms
Division Phaeophyta	brown algae
Division Euglenophyta	euglenoids
Division Chlorophyta	green plants
Subdivision Chlorophycophytina	green algae
Subdivision Embryophytina	embryo plants
Supraclass Bryophyta	bryophytes
Supraclass Tracheophyta	vascular plants

It is immediately apparent that nonvascular plants have representatives in all the divisions of plants. This means that there is a tremendous diversity in form, function, and physiology in this group. We will explore some of this diversity in the following chapters.

2

VIRUSES

AND

BACTERIA

A brief discussion of viruses is included here even though it is doubtful that they should be considered plants. It is even unimportant to us whether viruses are living organisms. Viruses have such considerable economic importance that everyone should be aware of these organisms as well as of the research being done on them.

VIRUSES

Viruses are the smallest and simplest of all known organisms. They are so small that they cannot be seen with the light microscope, and with but a few exceptions they readily pass through filters that prevent the passage of other organisms, including most bacteria. All viruses require living hosts in order to reproduce, and for a long time they were known as filterable, disease-producing organisms. With the aid of the electron microscope and modern research techniques, we now know much more about them, and have identified over three hundred different ones. They cause diseases in a wide variety of organisms, from bacteria to flowering plants to man. Because a virus is so small, its presence in an organism is detected only by its effect upon the host, and the host response is so specific that viruses are usually named either after the disease produced or after the host organism. Usually a single kind of virus infects only one type of host organism. A few representative viruses are poliomyelitis virus, influenza virus, smallpox virus, tobacco mosaic virus, and bacteriophages (viruses that attack bacteria).

General Characteristics

Viruses have very simple forms and structures. Commonly they are brick-shaped, spherical, or needle-shaped; some of the bacteriophages are differentiated into a head and a tail region (Fig. 2-1b). A mature

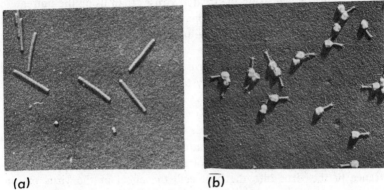

(a)   (b)

Fig. 2-1. *Left: Tobacco mosaic virus (magnified 55,000 times). Right: T_4 bacteriophage of Escherichia coli (magnified 40,000 times). Courtesy of the Virus Laboratory, University of California, Berkeley. Reproduced by permission.*

virus particle consists of two main parts: an outer protein coat and a nucleic acid core. Unlike other organisms, which have both the nucleic acids DNA and RNA, a single kind of virus has either DNA or RNA. Results from genetic studies, utilizing mutations and recombinations in certain DNA-containing bacteriophages, have indicated that the DNA contains linearly arranged genes. In these viruses, the DNA— probably a single molecule—corresponds to a normal chromosome of other organisms. Some of the larger viruses may also contain, in addition to nucleic acid and protein, a few molecules of lipids, carbohydrates, and enzymes.

The process of virus multiplication is unique in that viruses do not divide to form new individuals, as do other organisms. When a virus infects a host cell, it interferes with and redirects the metabolism of the host so that the host cell now makes new virus particles. How the virus controls the metabolism of the host is not completely understood. This process of virus multiplication in which the host makes new virus particles is termed *replication.*

Although a virus consists primarily of protein and nucleic acid, the entrance into the host of the nucleic acid alone is sufficient to establish infection. In studies with the tobacco mosaic virus (an RNA-containing virus—see Fig. 2-1a), it has been possible to treat the viruses so as to remove the protein coat from the nucleic acid. Subsequent infection by the naked RNA results in the formation of new virus particles by the host, complete with protein coats. However, the degree of infection is lower using the treated viruses than using the untreated. This result indicates that the protein coat might serve to protect the nucleic acid, or that it might facilitate the entry of the virus into the host cell, or both.

A striking feature of many viruses is that they can be crystallized from purified solutions. These crystals can then be dissolved in water and used to reinfect the host.

Bacteriophages

Bacteriophages (viruses that attack bacteria) are very useful research organisms. They are important in studies of the mode of entrance of the virus into the host cell, the effect of the virus on the host's metabolism, viral replication, and viral genetic systems. For these reasons, the bacteriophage-host relationship is discussed here in detail.

Many studies have been made on bacteriophages that lyse (disintegrate) the bacterium *Escherichia coli,* common in the intestine of man. These phages are differentiated into a head region, containing tightly coiled nucleic acid, and a tail (Fig. 2-1b). Most bacteriophages are DNA viruses; only a few RNA bacteriophages, of relatively recent discovery, are known. Several different kinds of coli-phages (viruses that attack *E. coli*), which differ primarily in the sizes of their tails, have been described. In order to initiate infection during experimental studies, phage particles and bacteria are mixed together in a suspension. This suspension is then spread evenly over the surface of an agar medium in Petri dishes. In 12 to 16 hours, clear areas (called *plaques*), which represent places where the phages have lysed bacterial cells, appear on the surface of the medium. Although bacteriophages are too small to be seen with the unaided eye or light microscope, the appearance of plaques locates places of phage infection and gives an indication of the intensity of infection.

During infection, the coli-phage becomes attached by its protein tail to the bacterial cell wall. However, the tail cannot become attached at every place on the wall. There are receptor sites present in the wall, and each kind of coli-phage can become attached only at its specific receptor sites. It is possible to obtain mutant phages that have lost their ability to become attached at their receptor sites, and, therefore, are unable to infect the cells.

Once attachment is made, a hole is dissolved in the bacterial cell wall and the viral DNA moves through the tail into the host. The details of this process are not yet clear. The protein coat remains outside the cell, attached to the wall. Inside the host cell, the phage DNA uncoils. The entrance of the virus DNA into the cell causes an immediate shift in the metabolism of the bacterium so that the host now makes phage nucleic acid and protein rather than normal bacterial compounds. In a matter of minutes, mature phage particles, complete with protein coats, appear in the cell. These phage particles can be seen with the electron microscope. Phage formation continues until a certain number have been formed. At this time the cell bursts, releasing the particles into the medium, where they can infect new bacterial cells.

The whole process, from infection to lysis, may take as little as 20 minutes. There are many details of this virus-host relationship that we still do not understand. For example, very little is known about how the virus controls and directs the host's metabolism. It is clear, however, that, except sometimes for the host's DNA, the structural elements or macromolecules of the bacterium are not broken down. This fact indicates that the virus takes over the control of the synthetic pathways of the host cell. How the virus takes over is unknown, but it is under active investigation.

BACTERIA

Bacteria or Schizophyta (schizo = fission, phyta = plants) are extremely common soil organisms and they are also abundant in the air, on skin, plants, and animals, and in fresh and salt water. Since most bacteria are less than 9 microns in length and are readily blown about by the wind, they are often troublesome airborne contaminants. Bacteria have even been collected several miles above the earth. The great economic importance of bacteria has contributed to the separation of the study of bacteria from botany, resulting in the establishment of departments of bacteriology in many universities. Bacteriologists are employed by federal, state, and local health agencies, universities, hospitals, sanitation and water departments, and chemical drug companies.

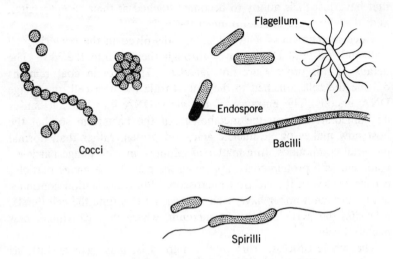

Fig. 2-2. *The various shapes of bacterial cells.*

Bacteria have relatively simple forms (Fig. 2-2). They are commonly rod-shaped (bacillus), spherical (coccus), or helical or slightly bent (spirillum). The cells of some bacteria form colonies of characteristic shape, and others, such as the actinomycetes, are filamentous. Although bacteria have simple forms, they are physiologically and biochemically diverse; species identification usually depends on studies of their metabolic characteristics in culture. These investigations involve *axenic* (only one kind of organism present) culturing of bacteria in liquid media or on solidified media. Most bacteria are *aerobic* organisms—they require the presence of molecular oxygen for growth. Other bacteria can live in the complete absence of oxygen, and may even be inhibited in growth by its presence. These are *anaerobic* bacteria, and they are present wherever putrefaction occurs.

Cellular Structure

Bacteria are the smallest organisms with a definite cellular organization. However, the cellular structure of bacteria differs greatly from that of other organisms (except the blue-green algae). The most striking feature of bacteria (and blue-green algae) is the absence of all double-membrane structures such as mitochondria, chloroplasts, and nuclei. Groups of enzymes are not compartmentalized in subcellular structures; the whole cell itself is the basic operational unit.

This type of cellular organization is considered to be primitive and has been termed *procaryotic*. On the other hand, organisms that possess double-membrane structures are termed *eucaryotic*. Figure 2-3 is a diagrammatic representation of a bacterial cell.

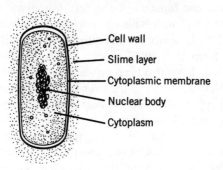

Cell wall

Slime layer

Cytoplasmic membrane

Nuclear body

Cytoplasm

Fig. 2-3. *Diagrammatic representation of a bacterial cell.*

Although mitochondria are absent, some of the respiratory enzymes normally associated with mitochondria are present, and are associated with the cytoplasmic membrane. Nuclear DNA is present in the form of a nuclear body, lacking enclosing membranes. Nuclear division is not a normal mitotic process; it appears to occur by constriction (amitosis) of the nuclear body into two nearly equal parts. Cell division generally occurs by the centripetal ingrowth of a crosswall, which divides the cell into approximately equal daughter cells. Subsequent cell enlargement is due primarily to protein synthesis: no aqueous vacuoles are present.

Some bacteria are capable of nuclear exchange followed by a type of gene segregation. This sexual phenomenon differs from that in eucaryotic organisms in that nuclear material is exchanged only in one direction, and only a part of the nuclear material is normally transferred. When two bacterial cells come together, the process is called *conjugation;* one cells acts as the donor and the other as the recipient. Most genetic studies in bacteria have been made on *Escherichia coli.* In this bacterium, the nuclear body contains a single linkage group, and is thus equivalent to a single chromosome of a eucaryotic organism.

The bacterial protoplast is surrounded by a rigid wall that contains both carbohydrates and amino acids. Bacteria may be separated into two large groups: gram-positive bacteria, which stain purple with Gram's stain, and gram-negative ones. Differences in staining behavior reflect differences in cell-wall composition. Gram's stain has wide utility in the identification of bacteria.

We are just beginning to understand the relationship of the cell wall to the form and function of the cell protoplast. It is possible to dissolve the bacterial wall with the enzyme lysozyme. The resultant naked protoplast is spherical in form even though it may have been derived from a bacillus species. With the use of other enzymes, protoplasts have also been obtained from fungi (such as yeasts and the mold *Neurospora*) and the liverwort *Marchantia*. These protoplasts are also spherical in form. Fungi and liverwort protoplasts appear to escape through pores in the cell wall prior to the complete dissolution of the wall. The cell wall, minus the enclosed protoplast, retains its normal shape, and it is evident that the wall, not the protoplast, determines the form of the cell. One interesting aspect of protoplast physiology is that we have not been able to induce protoplasts to synthesize a new cell wall. The significance of this is not yet fully understood. It has also been found that isolated protoplasts are quite sensitive to osmotic shock. On the other hand, protoplasts surrounded by a wall can withstand a wide range of osmotic pressures. The presence of a wall appears to be advantageous to cell survival in a changing environment.

A slime layer is usually present external to the cell wall (see Fig. 2-3). In some bacteria, the slime layer apparently helps prevent the cell from drying out. A thick, rigid slime layer is called a *capsule,* and in bacteria such as those that cause pneumonia (*Klebsiella pneumoniae*) and tuberculosis (*Mycobacterium tuberculosis*), the capsule seems to afford protection against body defense mechanisms.

Spores, which are structures resistant to elevated temperature and desiccation, are formed by relatively few bacteria. Spores develop within the bacterial cell (see Fig. 2-2), and are released upon disintegration of the cell wall. Spoilage of many types of home-canned foods is due to the survival during the canning process of spores of *Clostridium botulinum,* an anaerobic bacterium. Toxins formed by this bacterium produce the type of food poisoning known as botulism. In 1963, botulism poisoning was considered to be the cause of death of two women who had eaten tuna packed by a commercial cannery. Fortunately, contamination of commercially canned foods is an extremely rare occurrence.

Motile bacteria are propelled by means of one or more flagella (see

Fig. 2-2). As described in Chapter 1, bacterial flagella have a single fibril in cross section. Only a single type of protein is found in bacterial flagella, and it is of interest that the amino acid composition of this protein is similar to myosin, the contractile protein of animal muscle.

Modes of Nutrition

Based on nutritional capabilities, bacteria can be placed in two general classes: autotrophs and heterotrophs. Heterotrophic bacteria require for growth the presence of organic carbon compounds in the surrounding medium. They are unable to synthesize these compounds from carbon dioxide and thus cannot make their own food. Heterotrophic bacteria obtain these carbon compounds either from dead organic matter (saprobic bacteria) or from living organisms (parasitic bacteria). Not all heterotrophic bacteria, however, can readily be classified as either saprobes or parasites. Many bacteria pathogenic to man can also be cultured on artificial media in the laboratory. Organisms that usually live as parasites, but that may also exist as saprobes, are called *facultative* parasites.

Autotrophic organisms synthesize organic carbon compounds from carbon dioxide; they make their own food. Energy to drive these synthetic reactions is obtained either in the form of radiant energy from the sun (*photoautotrophic* bacteria) or by the oxidation of inorganic compounds (*chemoautotrophic* bacteria). The nutritional types of bacteria are described in more detail below.

Saprotism. Saprobes form the largest nutritional group of bacteria, and they are of great direct and indirect economic importance to man. Along with fungal saprobes, they are responsible for the decay and recycling of organic matter in nature. The free-living, nitrogen-fixing bacteria are saprobic organisms. Saprobic bacteria are also responsible for considerable food spoilage and food poisoning.

Many saprobic bacteria, however, are of direct benefit to man. They are important in the production of cheeses, sauerkraut, organic acids such as lactic and acetic acids, and alcohols. The antibiotics Aureomycin, bacitracin, Chloromycetin, and streptomycin are other important products of saprobic bacteria.

Parasitism. Parasitism is a form of *symbiosis* (broadly defined as the relationship of two organisms living in close association with each other) in which one organism lives at the expense of the other.

Bacterial parasites obtain nutrients from the host and, at the same time, have a harmful effect on the host. The adverse effect is generally due to the enzymatic destruction of host tissue, or to the formation of toxins that either diffuse from living bacterial cells or are released upon death of these cells. Numerous pathogenic bacteria of man, animals, and plants are known. Well-known bacterial diseases of man include cholera, diphtheria, bacterial pneumonia, plague, scarlet fever, tuberculosis, and whooping cough.

Photoautotrophism. Photosynthetic bacteria are a relatively small group of anaerobic organisms. Most of them utilize hydrogen sulfide in photosynthesis, a requirement that restricts their growth to specific ecological niches such as sulfur springs and black muds that contain decaying plant material. Two groups of photosynthetic bacteria are recognized: the green sulfur bacteria and the purple sulfur bacteria.

Bacterial photosynthesis differs from that of algae and other plants in several ways. First, the chlorophyll pigments of bacteria (there are at least two different chlorophyll pigments) are not identical to those of other plants. Second, hydrogen sulfide (H_2S) is used as a hydrogen donor by many of these bacteria. (Water is the hydrogen donor in algae and other plants.) Third, molecular oxygen is not a by-product of bacterial photosynthesis. An over-all reaction of bacterial photosynthesis is:

$$2H_2S + CO_2 \xrightarrow[\substack{radiant \\ energy}]{\substack{bacterial \\ chlorophyll}} (CH_2O) + 2S + H_2O$$

Radiant energy from sunlight is converted to chemical energy in the form of carbohydrates (CH_2O). Raw materials are carbon dioxide and a hydrogen donor such as hydrogen sulfide. Products of this reaction are carbohydrate, elemental sulfur (S), and water. Sulfur is deposited within the cell in purple sulfur bacteria and outside the cell in green sulfur bacteria.

The chlorophyll pigments of photosynthetic bacteria are not found in chloroplasts. The pigments are associated with submicroscopic, single-membraned structures called *chromatophores* (photosynthetic lamellae), which are commonly vesicular in form (Fig. 2-4). Recent studies have indicated that the photosynthetic membranes of some bacteria are continuous with, and arise by the invagination of, the

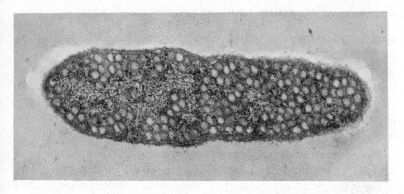

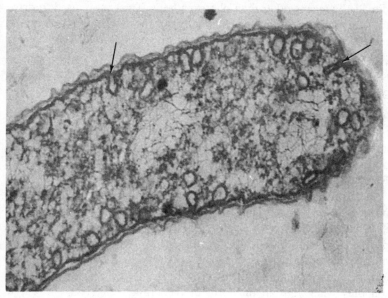

Fig. 2-4. *Electronmicrographs showing cellular organization of photosynthetic bacteria. Top: Rhodopseudomonas spheroides grown in a light intensity of 50 foot candles. The vesicular structures are photosynthetic membranes (chromatophores). Courtesy of Dr. G. Cohen-Bazire, University of California, Berkeley. Bottom: Rhodospirillum rubrum. Arrows indicate invaginated regions of the cell membrane. This section has been previously treated with the enzyme ribonuclease so that it will digest ribonucleic acid—a treatment that makes the cellular membranes more visible. Compare with top photo. From G. Cohen-Bazire and R. Kunisawa, "The Fine Structure of Rhodospirillum rubrum,"* Journal of Cell Biology, *Vol. 16 (1963), pp. 401–419. Reproduced by permission.*

cytoplasmic membrane. More research is needed on the structure of photosynthetic bacteria and on the relationship of structure to function. Photosynthetic bacteria have been useful research organisms in the study of the photosynthetic process, which is not as complex as in other plants. These bacteria are also of historical interest because the first understanding of the over-all photosynthetic reaction was obtained from studies on photosynthetic bacteria.

Chemoautotrophism. Chemoautotrophic bacteria are a unique nutritional group of aerobic organisms that obtain carbon (necessary in the synthesis of organic carbon compounds) directly from carbon dioxide by means other than photosynthesis. The energy used to drive these synthetic reactions is obtained from the oxidation of inorganic molecules such as nitrogen, sulfur, and iron compounds. Two energy-yielding reactions are:

$$NH_4^+ + 2O_2 \longrightarrow 2H_2O + NO_2^- + Energy \quad (Nitrosomonas)$$
$$2NO_2^- + O_2 \longrightarrow 2NO_3^- + Energy \quad (Nitrobacter)$$

Nitrosomonas and *Nitrobacter* are so-called nitrifying bacteria of the nitrogen cycle (described below). Other chemoautotrophic bacteria, known as iron bacteria, have been implicated in the origin of some of the economically important iron deposits, such as the Mesabi Range in Minnesota.

Heterotrophic and autotrophic bacteria are important because they participate in the recycling of organic matter. The involvement of bacteria in the nitrogen cycle is described here in detail because protein synthesis in all organisms depends on the availability of nitrogen compounds. The nitrogen cycle is diagrammed in Fig. 2-5. Many plants, including crop plants, obtain nitrogen rapidly from the soil only when it is in the form of the nitrate ion (NO_3^-). Large amounts of this ion are absorbed by plants from the soil, and the nitrogen is bound in plant proteins as an amino group ($-NH_2$). When eaten by animals, the nitrogen in plant proteins is incorporated into animal proteins. Upon the death of plants and animals, protein decomposition results in the formation and release into the soil of the ammonium ion (NH_4^+). Two types of aerobic bacteria, the so-called *nitrifying* bacteria, convert the ammonium ion to the nitrate ion. One type (*Nitrosomonas*) converts ammonium to the nitrite ion (NO_2^-), while the other type (*Nitrobacter*) converts nitrite to nitrate. This is the method whereby nitrates are made available to plants under natural conditions. Agriculture upsets this cycle when plants

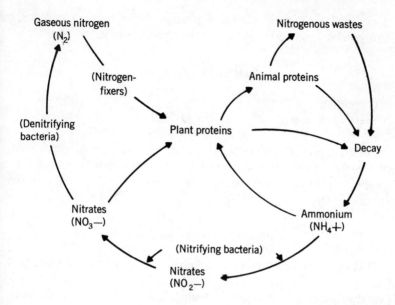

Fig. 2-5. *Simplified nitrogen cycle.*

are harvested and removed from the fields in which they grew. This agricultural procedure results in the continual depletion of nitrates (and other ions such as phosphates) from the soil; these nitrates must be replaced by the periodic addition of fertilizers to the soil.

Soil nitrate is also reduced in amount by the metabolic activities of many different anaerobic bacteria, called *denitrifying* bacteria. By a series of chemical reactions (reductions), these bacteria cause the nitrogen present in nitrates to be released to the atmosphere as nitrogen gas (N_2). Maintenance of aerobic conditions in fields, accomplished by proper soil drainage and tillage, tends to reduce the rate of denitrification.

Gaseous nitrogen is returned to the soil by a process called nitrogen fixation. Some of the nitrogen-fixing bacteria, such as the aerobic genus *Azotobacter* and the anaerobic genus *Clostridium,* are common, free-living soil organisms. Others live in symbiotic relationship with roots of many leguminous plants such as beans, clover, vetch, and alfalfa. Both free-living bacteria and symbiotic bacteria, which are found in so-called root nodules, incorporate gaseous nitrogen into bacterial amino acids and proteins. The process by which this is done is not well understood. Death of nitrogen-fixing bacteria makes the nitrogenous compounds in their cells available to other plants.

SUMMARY (Bacteria)

Photosynthetic pigments	Flagella	Food reserve
Bacterial chlorophylls	Single fibril in cross section	Variable

Additional: procaryotic cellular structure (no nuclear, mitochondrial, or chloroplast membranes); primarily nonphotosynthetic and heterotrophic organisms; amitotic nuclear division; conjugation type of sexuality.

RELATIONSHIPS (Bacteria)

Because of their procaryotic cellular structure, simple forms, and tremendous nutritional diversity, bacteria are believed to represent a primitive group of organisms. Although fossil bacteria have not been positively identified, the antiquity of bacteria is indicated by the presence of certain types of iron deposits over 500 million years old (Pre-Cambrian Age). These deposits are believed to have resulted from the metabolic activities of chemoautotrophic bacteria.

In regard to cellular structure, bacteria appear to be more closely related to blue-green algae than to any other organism. An evaluation of this relationship will be deferred until the blue-green algae have been discussed.

3

FUNGI

Fungi or Eumycota (eu = true, myketes = fungus) are nonphotosynthetic and depend on the products of other organisms, either living or dead, for food. Their ability to break down and utilize a wide variety of complex compounds accounts for their success in being able to live on a myriad of organic substrates. While fungi are ubiquitous as a group, the individual species usually are more limited in their nutritional tolerances. Fungi are of great economic importance. Some are parasites of animals and man. Many are virulent parasites of crop plants, resulting in considerable loss of food. Some fungi produce by-products such as antibiotics and organic acids, which are of use to man. Yeasts are indispensable to the baking and brewing industries. Characteristic flavors of cheeses result from the presence of certain fungi. For example, roquefort and Camembert cheeses are flavored (and colored) by the growths in the cheeses of *Penicillium roqueforti* and *P. camemberti,* respectively. A large industry is devoted to the culture of mushrooms for market. In addition, several fungi, such as the morels and truffles, are highly prized by gourmets.

THALLUS DIFFERENTIATION

The thallus of most fungi is differentiated into a vegetative portion and reproductive structures. In many fungi the vegetative part is not seen because it grows within the substrate; only the reproductive structures are visible. The vegetative portion is characteristically either unicellular (yeast-like) or filamentous (mold-like). However, some fungi may have both unicellular and filamentous growth phases, depending on environmental conditions. For example, *Mucor rouxii* exhibits mold-like growth under aerobic conditions and yeast-like growth under anaerobic conditions. In addition to change in form, there are changes in nutritional demands. For example, *M. rouxii* needs an exogenous supply of nicotinic acid when grown anaerobically. Although most cell-wall components are quantitatively similar, analysis has shown that yeast-like cell walls are distinctly higher in both the monosaccharide mannose and protein. Study has shown that anaerobic conditions *per se* do not cause mold-yeast dimorphism. Filamentous growth occurs under anaerobic conditions when the atmosphere is nitrogen. Anaerobic change in form occurs only when the carbon dioxide concentration is relatively high, and it has been found that the effective agent is the physically dissolved CO_2, not the bicarbonate ion in solution. Thus in *M. rouxii* it is possible to control experimentally the development of form by altering a single environmental factor.

The fact that CO_2 is a simple and specific morphogenetic agent has made *Mucor rouxii* useful for the study of changes in the biochemical machinery during form change. How does CO_2 alter cellular metabolism? It was found that glucose utilization (as an energy substrate) was essentially similar under both aerobic and anaerobic conditions: glycolysis was unimpaired. Therefore it was possible that anaerobically cultured cells would accumulate pyruvate, since oxygen is needed for respiration of pyruvate (to form CO_2 and water). However, no substantial increase in pyruvate was found. A link between the anaerobic utilization of pyruvate and the CO_2 effect was looked for. It is now known that organisms in general are capable of nonphotosynthetic incorporation of CO_2 into cellular constituents. Studies on *M. rouxii* have indicated that CO_2 is incorporated into cellular metabolites, particularly aspartic acid. It further appears that the malic enzyme is involved in CO_2 fixation in this fungus:

$$\text{pyruvate + carbon dioxide} \xrightarrow{\text{malic enzyme}} \text{malate}$$

The malate molecule is then metabolized and converted into aspartic acid. Presumably aspartic acid stimulates the synthesis and deposition of mannose and protein in the wall. It is of interest to note that aspartic acid is a prominent component of the mannan-protein portion of yeast cell walls. It is not yet known definitely how aspartic acid or mannan-protein influences mold-yeast dimorphism. One working hypothesis is that increased synthesis of mannan and protein disrupts or prevents orderly deposition of the cell-wall components necessary for filamentous growth. Elucidation of this awaits further research.

Fungal filaments, known as *hyphae* (singular: hypha), are usually highly branched and together are known as the *mycelium* (plural: mycelia) of the organism. Growth of hyphae is restricted to tips of filaments and usually is quite rapid. The mechanics of growth have been studied in the fungus *Neurospora,* and it has been found that protein synthesis is not restricted to the growing tip but occurs throughout the filament. Proteins formed in older parts subsequently are transferred to tips by active cytoplasmic streaming.

As hyphae grow, they continually come in contact with new substrates. Most organic substances are too large to pass directly through the cell wall and plasma membrane of the fungus. During growth there is a continuous secretion of enzymes into the substrate (these enzymes, therefore, are called *exoenzymes*). The enzymes break down the complex compounds into molecules small enough to enter the cell. Food not utilized immediately is stored in the form of the carbohydrate glycogen, or droplets of oil.

Reproductive structures of fungi are remarkable for their diversity of form and function, and identification of species of fungi is based largely on features of the reproductive structures. In general, little is known about the biochemical processes involved in the induction of reproduction in vegetative hyphae or the physiology of development of reproductive structures.

The spore is the most common type of reproductive unit in fungi. Spores are small, usually unicellular bodies that generally become detached from the parent plant. There are many different kinds of spores, and a single fungus may form more than one type during its development.

Most fungi produce spores during asexual reproduction. These are called *mitospores* because they result from mitotic divisions and thus may be either haploid or diploid. In aquatic fungi, spores usually are motile, propelled by means of one or two flagella. Flagellated mitospores are called *zoospores*. Spores of terrestrial fungi generally are nonflagellated and often are small and light enough to be disseminated by air currents. The conidium is the most common type of nonflagellated mitospore. Production of asexual spores results in a rapid buildup of a fungal population in a favorable area and the spread of the fungus to new regions. Spore formation generally begins soon after the organism becomes established on the substrate, and spores are produced continuously or in successive waves as long as environmental conditions (such as an adequate food supply) are favorable. Most asexual spores are thin-walled and are capable of immediate germination on a suitable substrate.

Spores produced after sexual reproduction are diploid and have a quite different function from asexual spores. Most sexual spores are thick-walled, dormant structures and have the primary function of enabling the organism to survive periods unfavorable to vegetative growth. They generally are produced at the end of the normal growing season, in the case of parasitic fungi, or when the food supply is diminished, in saprobic forms. Many of these spores cannot germinate until they have undergone periods of adverse conditions.

Many fungi produce a third type of spore. Such spores are formed immediately after meiosis, and are known as *meiospores*. Formation of these spores is discussed in more detail later. Function of these spores is similar to that of asexual spores; they aid in the dispersal to new areas. Moreover, since they develop after meiosis, these spores may carry new gene combinations that may make the fungi more virulent parasites or better adapted to a changing environment.

CLASSIFICATION

Fungi may be separated into eight more or less natural classes, of which only five are discussed here: Chytridiomycetes, Oömycetes, Zygomycetes, Ascomycetes, and Basidiomycetes. Separation is based mainly on details of sexual reproduction and form of flagellated cells, when present. (Fungi placed in the Chytridiomycetes, Oömycetes, and Zygomycetes were previously classified as Phycomycetes; but as more data became available it was evident that the Phycomycetes was an unnatural grouping. See Alexopoulos, listed in the Suggestions for Further Reading.) However, there are many fungi in which sexual reproduction has never been found; it is, therefore, impossible to place them with certainty in any of the groups above. These fungi, placed in a group called the Fungi Imperfecti, either have lost their ability to form sexual structures or have not yet been grown under the proper conditions to induce sexual reproduction. It is possible, too, that sexual reproduction has not been recognized. Thus constituted, Fungi Imperfecti is an artificial grouping of organisms and does not, therefore, have the same taxonomic meaning as the five groups above. Most of man's skin diseases, such as ringworm and athlete's foot, and a few of man's respiratory and other diseases are caused by these fungi. Identification of imperfect fungi depends mainly on details of asexual reproductive structures. Many of these fungi have asexual reproductive structures similar to those of Ascomycetes, but we cannot be sure that they are, in fact, Ascomycetes until sexual structures are found.

MODES OF NUTRITION

The nutritional requirements of fungi are the same as those of other plants, but fungi are heterotrophs since they cannot synthesize their own food. No autotrophic fungi are known, in contrast to bacteria. For energy sources, fungi utilize various organic carbon compounds, often simple sugars. The amount of nutrients present is not the only factor in determining whether a fungus will grow on a particular substance. The chemical nature of the substrate and its availability to the fungus are also important. Fungi that thrive in slightly acid media may be completely inhibited on neutral or slightly basic substances. The reverse may be true for other fungi. This knowledge has been used to control the growth of some fungi. Fungi generally require the presence in the medium of one or more complex organic growth factors (such as vitamins) for growth. Absence of these factors inhibits growth even though sufficient available organic carbon compounds are present.

Fungi do more than merely absorb food; they also affect the physical and chemical nature of the substrate on which they grow. In some instances such as in brewer's yeast, they modify their environment so that they can no longer grow, even though nutrients are still available. During respiration, brewer's yeast metabolizes sugars and gives off ethyl alcohol into the medium as a by-product. Unfortunately for the yeast, the concentration of alcohol increases to a level that is lethal to the yeast.

Fungi have long been divided into two major groups—saprobes and parasites—depending on their mode of nutrition. Not all fungi readily fit in either of these two categories. Although most fungi are either strict saprobes or obligate parasites (absolute requirement for a living host), there are some that can grow on both living and dead material. These fungi are known as facultative parasites or facultative saprobes. Moreover, there is an additional type of symbiotic relationship found in fungi. Some fungi form associations with other plants, vascular and nonvascular, in which both partners benefit. This symbiotic relationship is termed *mutualism*.

Saprotism

Fungal saprobes, along with those of bacteria, are scavengers of the plant kingdom. They utilize numerous organic compounds from simple sugars to complex organic carbon substances, making energy tied up in these molecules available for growth and development. Saprobes have considerable influence on our daily lives. Many are important agents of food spoilage. Molds on bread, jelly, jam, and syrup are familiar examples, although not as common as formerly because of the addition of various growth retardants to foodstuffs. Others are important in food processing, such as the baking and cheese industries, and in the production of organic acids and alcohols. Wherever humidity is high, saprobes are particularly troublesome, because they rapidly degrade leather, paper, textiles, and even insulation on electrical appliances.

Saprobic fungi are also of considerable importance to foresters and lumbermen. A large number of wood-rotting fungi, mostly Basidiomycetes, are known. Many of them rot the wood of living and growing trees while they are still standing. In many cases, the vegetative mycelium completely rots the inside of trees before there is any external evidence of fungal infection. These trees are worthless to the lumber industry. Moreover, infected trees occupy valuable space and serve as reservoirs for the spread of the fungus to other trees. Although a fungus that attacks standing trees might also be expected to break down wood of fallen trees, it seldom does. Fallen trees are usually decayed by different fungi.

Parasitism

Parasitic fungi have plagued man ever since he changed from a nomadic to an agricultural existence. Practically all plants of use to man have one or more fungal parasites. As in the cases of bacterial diseases, fungi may be pathogenic and quickly kill the host, or they may have a balanced relationship in which they obtain nutrients from the plant without killing it. Plant parasites are not confined to any one group, but have representatives in all groups, including the Fungi Imperfecti.

There are three general ways in which a fungal parasite grows in and obtains nutrients from its host. In some of the simpler, unicellular fungi, an individual derived from a single spore will enter and infect only one cell of the host. Its whole development is confined to this single cell. Parasites of this type are common on algae, other fungi, and roots of flowering plants. The degree of infection depends on the number of spores in the surrounding medium. Many of these fungi are host specific, and there is evidence to indicate that the host exudes into the medium specific substances that attract the motile spores of the fungus.

Most parasitic fungi are filamentous, and their growth is not restricted to the confines of a single host cell. In many of these, hyphae predominantly grow between the cells of the host in the region of the middle lamella, and hence are termed *intercellular* hyphae. Short, lateral filaments, called *haustoria,* grow into adjacent cells from these intercellular hyphae and function as nutrient-absorbing structures (Fig. 3-1). Fungi that absorb nutrients over long periods of time

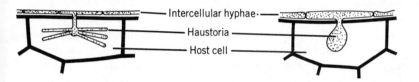

Fig. 3-1. *Diagrammatic representation of two forms of fungal haustoria.*

without killing the host usually possess this kind of hyphal differentiation. In other mycelial parasites, hyphae grow through cell lumens as well as cell walls, often causing complete tissue destruction. Many of these are destructive plant parasites.

A few parasitic fungi are of historical interest because they affected the economies and development of whole nations. Of considerable importance is *Phytophthora infestans* (*phytophthora* literally means "plant devourer"), an Oömycete that causes the disease called "late blight of potatoes." Just as our economy is based on the cereal grain, the Irish economy was based on the potato. The great Irish famine, beginning in 1845, was brought about by the destruction of the potato crop by the fungus. Over a million people died as a result of the famine, and more than that number emigrated to different lands, principally the United States and Canada. This fungus is still an ever present danger in Ireland as well as in other potato-growing areas, but means are available to control the disease.

Another Oömycete, *Plasmopara viticola,* which causes downy mildew of grape, nearly ruined the French wine industry during the 1870s and 1880s. It lives on the leaves, stems, and fruits of the grape plant, obtaining nutrients from host cells by means of haustoria. A native of North America, where the grapes were relatively unaffected by it, *Plasmopara* was accidentally introduced into Europe. There the cultivated grapes were highly susceptible, and they sustained considerable damage. The mildew was not controlled until 1885 when a fungicide known as Bordeaux mixture (a dilute solution of copper sulfate and lime) came into use. This is the first reported use of a fungicide, and it is still in use today.

Most parasitic fungi, however, have not been so drastic in their effect as the two examples above. Nonetheless, they all are ever present problems and the seriousness of infection of any particular parasite depends on a combination of factors, including temperature, humidity, methods of crop cultivation, and kinds of control procedures used. The field of plant pathology is concerned primarily with the biology of fungal parasites. There are plant pathology departments in most large universities, and state and federal governments support research of many plant pathologists in field stations and other installations. Although the primary objective is to prevent and control plant diseases, plant pathologists also engage in research of a more fundamental nature.

Besides the plant parasites, many fungi parasitize man, producing diseases generally termed *mycoses*. Often erroneously considered to be mainly tropical diseases, mycoses are common in the temperate climates as well. Many of these produce unsightly lesions of the skin, and some may result in death. Several types of "ringworm" are among the more familiar kinds of mycoses in the United States. In many cases, effective and specific control treatments are unknown. There are few antibiotics effective against fungi, in contrast to the many available against parasitic bacteria. This should be a promising area of future research.

Insects also have fungal parasites. One fungus lives on the common housefly in the more humid parts of the United States. Upon entry, the fungal mycelium grows throughout the body of the fly; just before the fly's death, which occurs within a week, the fly attaches itself firmly by its proboscis to a surface such as a windowpane. Shortly thereafter, asexual reproductive structures of the fungus emerge from the insect's body and spore discharge ensues. Attempts to use fungal parasites of insects for biological control have generally been unsuccessful.

A few parasitic fungi are remarkable in that they trap their prey, which may be amoebae, rhizopods, or nematodes (eel worms), by either adhesive or mechanical means. Adhesive traps may consist of hyphal branches, spherical knobs at tips of short hyphae (which have been referred to as lethal lollipops), or hyphal rings or loops. Surfaces of the traps are coated with an adhesive substance to which the prey stick on contact. Certainly one of the most complex traps, a mechanical one, is produced by *Dactylella* (Fig. 3-2). It is shaped

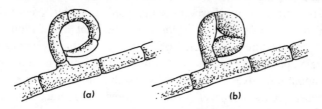

Fig. 3-2. *Traps of the predaceous fungus Dactylella. (a) Open. (b) Swollen.*

like a noose and is triggered when a straying nematode attempts to move through it. Cells of the noose swell considerably on stimulation, trapping the nematode. Subsequently, fungal filaments grow into and absorb nutrients from the nematode.

Predaceous fungi are not necessarily obligate predators. They are isolated from the soil with ease and grow on a variety of complex organic media in axenic culture. Studies on *Arthrobotrys conoides* have shown that this fungus seldom forms traps when grown in axenic culture. However, traps readily form when nematodes, or water in which nematodes have been growing, or tissue extracts of nematodes, are added to the fungus culture. Thus we have a situation where the prey itself induces morphological change in the predator— a change necessary for the prey-predator relationship. There is evidence that the specific morphogenetic agent is of low molecular weight and that it is probably a peptide or an amino acid. Hopefully, future research will identify this agent and clarify its involvement in the biochemistry of form development.

Mutualism

Mutualistic associations involving fungi and other plants are of considerable biological interest. In the preceding section we saw that many fungi obtain nutrients from living hosts. It is somewhat surprising to find that certain fungi are also of benefit to their symbiont.

Recent experimental studies have been directed toward the elucidation of the nature of this fungal benefit. Two types of mutualistic relationships will be described: (1) mycorrhizae—associations of fungi and roots of vascular plants—and (2) lichens—associations of fungi and algae.

Mycorrhizae. The mycorrhizal (mykes = fungus, rhiza = root) state is world-wide in distribution and has been found in the majority of seed-bearing plants studied. One investigator has even reported that it is present in all woody plants studied so far. Many different fungi are capable of establishing a mycorrhizal association, and, in some cases, different species of fungi can form mycorrhizae with a single species of seed-plant. Many of these are common soil fungi that apparently live as saprobes; the establishment of this association probably occurs whenever a root tip comes in contact with a receptive fungus. Two distinctive types of root-fungus relationships are found. In one type, the fungal mycelium forms a mantle on the surface of the root; only a few intercellular hyphae penetrate the root itself. In the second type, most of the hyphae live intracellularly within the root.

Even though mycorrhizae are of widespread occurrence, the nature of the interaction between fungal and nonfungal symbionts is not completely clear. Various theories have been proposed to explain this relationship. There is little doubt that in most cases fungi obtain organic compounds from nonfungal members. This has led to the suggestion that their relationship is essentially one of parasitism. Perhaps in some instances, especially in those in which the fungus lives primarily within root tissue, this suggestion might be true. However, there is considerable evidence to indicate that in most cases these associations are beneficial to vascular plants. Most of this information comes from studies on conifers such as the pine. Cases have been reported in which trees with mycorrhizae grow better than those without. It has also been shown that mycorrhizal trees accumulate more inorganic salts than those without. Furthermore, in experiments utilizing radioactive tracer compounds, it has been shown that compounds absorbed by fungal hyphae can be transferred to the associated root. In these instances, the fungus apparently benefits its symbiont by increasing mineral salt absorption. It has also been suggested that fungi provide growth-promoting substances to the seed plant. Of course, further experimental work is necessary before any broad generalizations can be formulated to explain the beneficial effects of mycorrhizae.

Lichens. When algae and fungi grow together to form lichens, the resulting thalli usually are entirely different from those of either organism alone. Thalli are commonly "leafy" (foliose), encrusting, or shrubby. Lichens are widespread, being found in arid and arctic regions as well as in temperate and tropical areas. They commonly grow on bare soil, tree trunks, branches, fence posts, unweathered granitic rocks, and other exposed places. Lichens can be white, black, or various shades of red, orange, yellow, or green. Some green lichens are often confused with bryophytes, especially liverworts. Colors are due to the accumulation in the thallus of various pigments, often different lichenic acids.

Some lichens are economically important. Arctic reindeer and caribou feed on extensive patches of reindeer "mosses" that are lichens. Man apparently has eaten lichens for food only in emergencies. Prior to the discovery of coal tars, lichens were the sources of numerous dyestuffs. The only important dyestuff now obtained is used in the preparation of litmus paper for chemistry. This dye turns blue in basic solutions and red in acid solutions. Of more recent interest is the discovery that some lichens produce substances that act as antibiotics against many gram-positive bacteria not affected by the common antibiotics, and against some fungi.

The simplest lichen thallus consists of relatively few fungal cells growing among algal cells. In most lichens, however, the fungus is the dominant organism and the thallus has a definite internal structure (Fig. 3-3). In these lichens, algae are restricted to a definite layer between a compact upper fungal layer and a loose fungal layer below. In some lichens (as in Fig. 3-3), an additional compact fungal layer is present on the lower surface of the thallus. Lichens contain either green or blue-green algae. The majority of lichen fungi are Ascomycetes, but a few are Basidiomycetes or Fungi Imperfecti. Although composite structures, lichens are given binomial names comparable to those of other organisms. However, the name, which is based on fungal reproductive structures, belongs to the fungal component only; the algae are similar to already named, free-living ones. The implication that each lichen possesses a different fungus needs experimental verification.

The nature of the relationship between algae and fungi in lichens is not fully explained. Some earlier workers suggested that this asso-

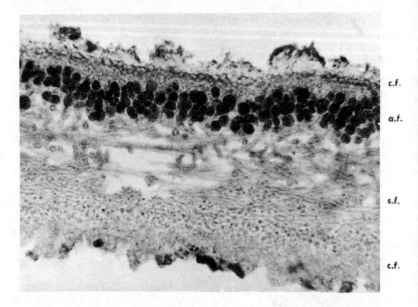

c.f.

a.f.

s.f.

c.f.

Fig. 3-3. *Section of a lichen. The darkly stained bodies are algal cells.* c.f.: *compact fungal zone;* a.f.: *algal and fungal zone;* s.f.: *spongy fungal zone.*

ciation is a parasitic one. They noted that in many lichens the fungal haustoria are tightly appressed to—or actually penetrate—the algal cells. Although fungi undoubtedly obtain organic compounds from the algae, simple parasitism does not explain the extremely stable relationship and longevity of lichens under natural conditions, nor does it explain the resultant highly differentiated internal structure of most lichens. Although certainly not conclusive, present evidence indicates that fungi aid in mineral salt absorption or exchange metabolites with the algae. There is no evidence to support the commonly held belief that the fungi protect the algae against desiccation. Unfortunately, critical culture work has been done on very few lichens.

CHYTRIDIOMYCETES

Fungi placed in this group have reproductive cells each with a single posterior, whiplash flagellum. The vegetative bodies of some are unicellular and may lack a cell wall during certain stages of development. Depending on environmental conditions, the entire cell is converted into either a sporangium (a spore-producing structure) or a gametangium (a gamete-producing structure). Other Chytridiomycetes (such as *Allomyces*) are filamentous, and reproductive structures develop on their hyphal branches. Only the general form and development of *Allomyces* will be discussed here.

Allomyces

Species of *Allomyces* are aquatic organisms, common in (but not restricted to) warmer regions such as the tropics. They are plant and animal saprobes and often can be "captured" on boiled hemp or sesame seeds (or other suitable substrates) by covering dried soil with water and adding a few seeds for bait. If *Allomyces* is present in the soil, white hyphae will grow from the seed in a few days. Closer examination shows that the mycelium is differentiated into (1) rhizoidal filaments that penetrate the substrate and absorb nutrients, and (2) filaments that extend away from the substrate and bear gametangia (Fig. 3-4a). Male and female gametangia are borne on the same filament and in some species have a consistent spatial relationship to each other. The male gametangium is colored orange due to the presence of carotenoid pigments in the male gametes. The female gametes are colorless.

The presence of both male and female gametangia on the same filament, often in adjacent cells, indicates that sex determination in *Allomyces* is probably not under direct gene control, but is under extranuclear or cytoplasmic control. In many plants, animals, and man, sex determination is under gene control. What are the biochemical mechanisms involved in sex determination in organisms? Little is known about this basic problem. In *Allomyces* it has been suggested that carotenes (found here only in the male gametangium) might be the cause of sex differences. But it is more probable that carotene synthesis is the result, not the cause, of sex differences. More recent investigations show that female gametes have more RNA than do male gametes and that it is possible to alter the sex ratio in favor of male gametangia by experimentally interfering with RNA synthesis. Perhaps future research will indicate how RNA is involved in sex determination.

Gamete formation occurs by cleavage of the multinucleate cytoplasm into uninucleate male or female gametes in their respective gametangia. Mature gametes are discharged through one or more pores that develop in the gametangium wall: the gametes possess a

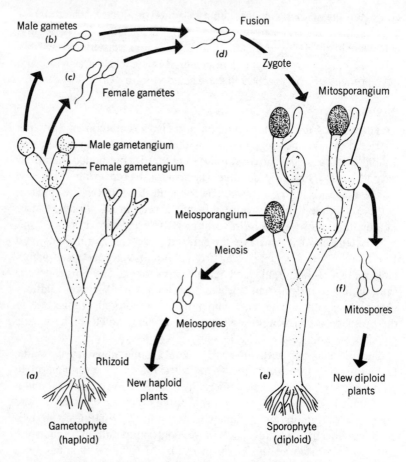

Fig. 3-4. *Life history of Allomyces.*

single posterior, whiplash flagellum (Fig. 3-4b, c). The orange-colored male gamete, smaller and more actively motile than the female, is attracted to the female gamete, which secretes a hormone called "sirenin." Sirenin has been partially purified, but its molecular structure is not completely known. It would be of interest to know its mode of action on the male gamete.

Fusion of gametes results in the formation of a zygote, which is propelled for a short time by two flagella, one contributed by each gamete. The zygote settles down on a suitable substrate, loses its flagella, and germinates into a new mycelium. The diploid mycelium is nearly identical in form to the haploid plant; thus *Allomyces* is said to have an "alternation of isomorphic generations." However, the reproductive structures on the diploid plant have quite different functions from those on the haploid. Two kinds of reproductive organs develop: *mitosporangia* and *meiosporangia*. Mitosporangia (Fig. 3-4e) are thin-walled and colorless, and they give rise to uniflagellate, diploid mitospores. Mitospore production results in a rapid population buildup in a short time period.

Meiosporangia (Fig. 3-4e) have brownish cell walls and are resistant structures. They enable *Allomyces* to survive conditions unfavorable for vegetative growth—as, for example, when a pond in which it is growing dries up. These are the structures that would be present in the dry-soil samples mentioned above. When conditions are favorable for growth (such as when dry soil is placed in water), each nucleus in the resistant sporangium (there are usually 12) undergoes meiosis to form four haploid meiospores. The meiospores, each with a single posterior, whiplash flagellum, emerge from the ruptured sporangium and swim around until they come in contact with a suitable substrate. Being haploid, meiospores give rise to haploid, gamete-producing plants. This explains why gamete-producing plants (gametophytes) are the first plants to appear in a new *Allomyces* culture, whereas the spore-producing plants (sporophytes) do not appear until later.

OÖMYCETES

In contrast to fungi in the previous group, Oömycetes produce biflagellate mitospores (zoospores), each with one whiplash and one tinsel flagellum. Gametangia are of two morphologically dissimilar types: the male organ, called an *antheridium,* and the female organ, or *oögonium* (Fig. 3-5e). In most cases, gametangia are produced on specialized hyphal branches. In a few, the entire thallus (which in this case is unicellular) is converted into a gametangium.

Several Oömycetes are of considerable economic importance; some are among the most destructive parasites known. *Phytophthora infestans,* the cause of late blight of potato, and *Plasmopara viticola,* the cause of downy mildew of grapes, have already been discussed. *Saprolegnia* will be used as an example of this fungal class.

Saprolegnia

Species of *Saprolegnia* are among the most common of the freshwater molds. Although a few are parasitic—for example, on fish—most are saprobes of dead animals. A common method to obtain *Saprolegnia* for study is to add a dead fly or a boiled and split seed to water that contains a small amount of soil. If *Saprolegnia* is present, the fly will become surrounded by a halo of hyphae in a few days. The hyphae remain in the vegetative condition as long as abundant food is available. Diminution of nutrients results first in the formation of mitosporangia (also called *zoosporangia*) and later in the development of gametangia and zygospores.

Vegetative hyphae are rather coarse and tubular in *Saprolegnia*. At the onset of asexual reproduction, hyphal tips become filled with cytoplasm and are cut off by cross walls from the rest of the hyphae. The hyphal tips are transformed into mitosporangia, and mitospores (zoospores) are formed by the cleavage of the multinucleate cytoplasm within the sporangia (Fig. 3-5a). Mature zoospores are discharged through an apical pore and differ from those of *Allomyces* in that they possess two anterior flagella—one whiplash and one tinsel. After a period of motility, zoospores lose their flagella and encyst. Upon germination, each cyst gives rise to a single biflagellated spore, but now the flagella are laterally inserted (Fig. 3-5b–d). Zoospores are capable of repeated encystment and emergence if a suitable substrate is not present. Zoospores function to produce new plants on new nutrient sources.

As available nutrients continue to decrease, a further shift in hyphal metabolism results in the development of sexual reproductive structures. Species of *Saprolegnia* are *hermaphroditic* (male and female sex organs are on a single plant) and *homothallic* (sexual structures on a single thallus are self-compatible). Male and female gametangia are highly specialized in function (Fig. 3-5e). The male structure (antheridium) produces sperm nuclei; the female gametangium (oögonium) produces eggs. During sexual reproduction a hyphal branch, which produces the antheridium, grows toward and comes in contact with the developing oögonium. (The interaction of hormones during sexual reproduction has been demonstrated in a related fungus, *Achlya ambisexualis,* by Dr. John Raper—see Suggestions for Further Reading.) Fertilization tubes, through which

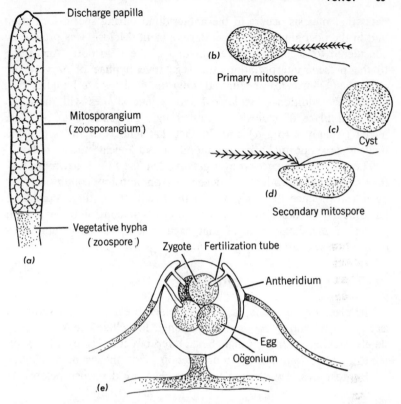

Fig. 3-5. *Saprolegnia.* (*a–d*) *Stages in asexual reproduction.* (*e*) *Sexual reproduction.*

sperm nuclei pass, grow into the oögonium and come in contact with the eggs.

The diploid zygote produced by fusion of gamete nuclei develops a thick wall about itself and becomes a dormant structure called a *zygospore*. Produced at a time when nutrient supply has diminished, the zygospore functions to tide the organism over a period of adverse conditions. Zygospores can survive long periods of desiccation. Upon germination, the zygote gives rise to new vegetative hyphae.

You will note that no attempt to identify haploid and diploid structures was made in the account above. Fusion of sperm nucleus with egg nucleus establishes the diploid phase. The most recent evidence from genetic and cytological studies on Oömycetes in general indicates that meiosis occurs in the antheridium during sperm formation and in the oögonium during egg development. Meiosis was previously considered to occur during germination of the zygospore. According to the present interpretation, the vegetative hyphae of *Saprolegnia* and other Oömycetes are diploid; only the gametes are haploid. It is hoped that additional cytological and genetic studies will show the time and place of meiosis in these fungi. The small size of fungi nuclei (usually 2 to 3 μ) and the fact that mitosis occurs within the nuclear envelope make interpretation of cytological studies difficult.

The general sequence from vegetative hyphae to asexual reproduction to sexual reproduction, depending on nutrient conditions, has been known since the early part of the twentieth century. Very little has since been done to elucidate factors that control these growth phases or metabolic changes that occur within the mycelium as a result of these changes.

ZYGOMYCETES

The class Zygomycetes includes the black bread molds, several insect parasites, and a few predaceous fungi. Flagellated cells are completely lacking in these fungi. Sexual reproduction is by means of gametangial fusion; asexual reproduction is by means of nonflagellated mitospores. Two examples of this class are described below.

Rhizopus

The most common species of *Rhizopus* is the black bread mold. In contrast to *Allomyces* and *Saprolegnia,* which grow in water, species of *Rhizopus* are specialized for life on land. The mycelium is differentiated into three functional types (Fig. 3-6a). One type of hypha, called a *stolon,* rapidly grows over the surface of the substrate. *Rhizoidal branches* arise at certain places on the stolon, and they grow into and break down organic material of the substrate. A third type of hyphal branch, the *sporangiophore,* grows into the air and supports a terminal sporangium. Mitospores (also called sporangiospores) developed within sporangia are nonflagellated and are wind-disseminated. They are small, dark-colored, and light in weight, and may remain suspended in the air for considerable periods of time. Sporangiophores aid spore dispersal in that they elevate sporangia above the level of the substrate.

Rhizopus is heterothallic but, because gametangia are morphologically similar, it is not possible to identify male and female plants.

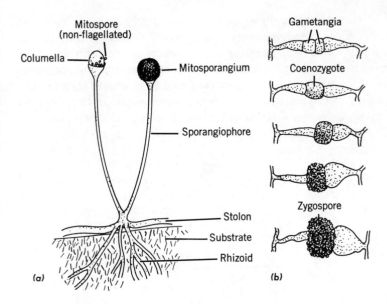

Fig. 3-6. *Rhizopus.* (*a*) *Hyphal differentiation and asexual repro-duction.* (*b–f*) *Stages in formation of coenozygote.*

Therefore one sex is referred to as the plus strain and the other as the minus strain. So long as the strains are grown separated, no sexual reproductive structures are formed. When both strains are cultured together and the hyphae are in close proximity to each other, short lateral branches develop and grow together. Upon contact, the tip of each hypha is cut off by a cross wall to form a multinucleate game-tangium. Cell walls between adjacent plus and minus gametangia then are broken down and the protoplasts of the two cells fuse to form a *coenozygote* (a coenozygote is a multinucleate zygote). This cell de-velops a thick, black, warty wall, and is called a zygospore (Fig. 3-6b–f). It is a dormant structure that is exceedingly difficult to germi-nate. Meiosis occurs during zygospore germination. Upon germina-tion, a single sporangiophore emerges from the ruptured zygospore and nonflagellated haploid spores are wind-disseminated.

Pilobolus

It has been mentioned that fungi live on practically all known or-ganic substrates, and the dung of animals is no exception. *Pilobolus,* common on dung of such herbivores as cows and horses, is one of the most remarkable of these coprophilous (dung-loving) fungi. Although many such fungi show various modifications for their habitat, *Pilobolus* exhibits an amazing specialization in the form and function of its asexual reproductive apparatus (sporangium plus sporangiophore). Not only does the sporangiophore bend toward light (phototropism) but, at maturity, the whole sporangium is forcibly shot away by a "water-squirt" mechanism. The mature sporangial apparatus prior to discharge is shown in Fig. 3-7.

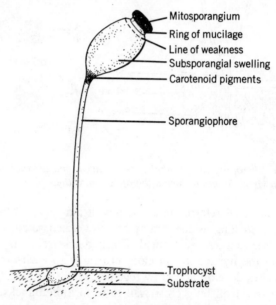

Fig. 3-7. *Mature sporangial apparatus of Pilobolus.*

The mature sporangium wall is black and is impregnated with a waxy compound. The black color apparently helps prevent light damage to the colorless spores. Within the sporangium, spores are in the upper part and a ring of mucilage is below. Immediately prior to discharge, the sporangium wall near the base of the sporangium breaks, exposing the mucilage. The mucilage plays a role in a later stage of sporangial discharge.

The sporangiophore is a remarkable example of cell specialization for function. It is responsible for the directed, forcible discharge of the sporangium. The sporangiophore arises from a bulbous base at or near the level of the substrate. Unlike *Rhizopus, Pilobolus* has cross walls separating the sporangiophore from the rest of the mycelium. The upper end of the sporangiophore is enlarged, forming a sub-sporangial swelling. An orange carotenoid pigment found at the base of the subsporangial swelling is involved in the phototropic behavior of the sporangiophore. The sporangiophore bends toward the direction of highest light intensity. Around the upper part of the sub-sporangial swelling there is a line of weakness where the cell wall is thinner in the rigid carbohydrate wall.

Protoplasm within the sporangiophore is restricted to a thin peripheral layer by a large central vacuole. Osmotically active sugars in the vacuole cause water pressure to build up in the sporangiophore. When the pressure reaches a certain point, the sporangiophore bursts (with an audible "pop") at the line of weakness, shooting away the sporangium for distances up to several feet. (*Pilobolus* literally means "hat-thrower.") The photo-orientation of the sporangiophore makes it almost certain that the sporangium will be shot clear of the substrate.

Upon contact with an object, the sporangium becomes firmly affixed to it by the mucilage at the base of the sporangium. If the object happens to be a blade of grass or other suitable substance, there is a good chance that it, and the sporangium, will be eaten by a herbivore. Inside the animal, the spores are acted upon by substances in the digestive tract, altering the physiology of the spores so that they are capable of germination. Thus the developmental cycle of *Pilobolus* is again initiated.

ASCOMYCETES

The Ascomycetes (askos = sac) form a very large group that contains many economically important fungi. Most of the blue-green, red, and brown molds that cause food spoilage are Ascomycetes. Many, including the powdery mildews, are plant parasites. Ergot of rye, one of the oldest known plant diseases and one recognized by the Greeks and Romans, is caused by the fungus *Claviceps purpurea*. Infection of the rye plant by the fungus occurs at the time of flowering and results in the replacement of kernels of rye by a hard, black fungal growth that contains several potent alkaloids. Although they may cause gangrene and death if eaten in large amounts, these alkaloids have important medicinal uses. They are used in the control of hemorrhage, especially during childbirth, and in treating migraine.

Another Ascomycete, of more recent notoriety, causes the Dutch elm disease. Accidental introduction of the fungus *Ceratocystis ulmi* into the United States is gradually eradicating the American elm, one of our most beautiful shade trees. This particular fungus has been difficult to control because it lives within the tree, where sprays cannot reach it. Spread is due to bark-boring beetles, which carry fungal spores from tree to tree. Most control measures have been directed toward the beetle but, except in a few cases, have largely been unsuccessful.

Although few Ascomycetes are used as food, the morels and truffles are more highly prized by gourmets than are mushrooms (which are Basidiomycetes). Unfortunately it has so far been impossible to culture morels and truffles for commerce. Truffles are of particular interest because they are found below the soil surface in presumed mycorrhizal association with trees such as oaks. And because they grow below the soil surface, they are often difficult to find. Although these fungi have a characteristic odor, man's sense of smell is too poorly developed to detect it. Therefore, in France and Italy, pigs and dogs have been trained for truffle hunting. Our native truffles, found by hand sifting of soil, are usually quite small, but large imported ones may be purchased in gourmet sections of many stores in the United States.

Except in a few cases in which the plant body is unicellular, Ascomycetes are typically mycelial. New cells arise by the forward growth of hyphal tips, with subsequent ingrowth of new septa behind the tips. The septa do not form complete walls; a central pore remains which allows for cytoplasmic interchange between adjacent cells as well as for movement of both mitochondria and nuclei.

While there is general uniformity in hyphal structure in this group, there is great morphological diversity among reproductive bodies. Several types of asexual reproductive structures are known, each of which is adapted to a particular function. A type of mitospore called a *conidium* is one of the most common types. Conidia are uninucleate, nonflagellated cells cut off in chains from tips of modified hyphae called *conidiophores*. Airborne conidia are characteristic of many common food-spoilage fungi such as *Aspergillus* and *Penicillium* (Fig. 3-8).

The structures (fruiting bodies) resulting from sexual reproduction vary more than those associated with asexual reproduction. But before these structures can be discussed, the sexual process in Ascomycetes should first be mentioned. Sexual reproduction is generally

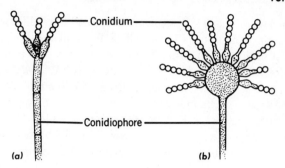

Fig. 3-8. (a) *Conidiophore of Penicillium.* (b) *Section of a conidiophore of Aspergillus.*

initiated by fusion of the cytoplasm of a male cell with that of a female (Fig. 3-9). The one or more nuclei present in the male cell move into the female cell and pair with the nuclei, but without fusion.

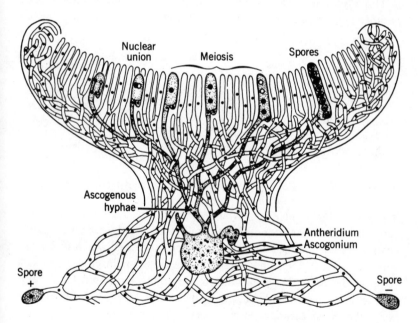

Fig. 3-9. *Diagram of the structure of the fruiting body of an Ascomycete. Ascogonium = female cell; antheridium = male cell; ascogenous hyphae = dikaryotic hyphae. From L. W. Sharp,* Fundamentals of Cytology (*McGraw-Hill Book Co., Inc., 1943*). *Reproduced by permission.*

After pairing, the nuclei divide mitotically, and hyphal filaments grow out from the female cell. Each cell of these filaments contains one nucleus of each parental type. The condition in which a cell contains two paired nuclei, one from each parent, is called *dikaryotic*. Although nuclear fusion has not occurred, dikaryotic cells are functionally diploid. (Cells that contain one or more unpaired nuclei, all of the same type, are called *monokaryotic*.) As dikaryotic hyphae grow and branch, the surrounding parental monokaryotic hyphae also grow and intermingle with the dikaryotic hyphae, ultimately forming a fruiting body. The form of the fruiting body is a diagnostic feature of many fungi in this group. The directed and integrated growth of dikaryotic and monokaryotic hyphae has not yet been fully investigated. At maturity, terminal cells of dikaryotic hyphae form sac-like structures called *asci* (singular: *ascus*), usually in specific regions of the fruiting body.

Three general forms of fruiting bodies are recognized: apothecium, perithecium, and cleistothecium (Fig. 3-10). Basically the apothecium

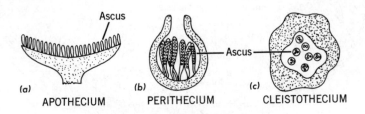

Fig. 3-10. *The three basic types of Ascomycete fruiting bodies.*

is cup-shaped (as in *Peziza*), and asci line the inner surface of the cup. Fruiting bodies of morels and truffles are considered to be modifications of the apothecium. The perithecium is usually a flask-shaped structure with a neck and an apical opening. In this type, asci develop at the base. The fungi that cause ergot of rye and Dutch elm disease have perithecial fruiting bodies. The third type of fruiting body, the cleistothecium, is completely enclosed, and asci are scattered throughout the interior. A common example of a fungus having cleistothecia is *Microsphaeria*, which causes powdery mildew of lilac.

The ascus is the definitive characteristic of Ascomycetes. In most Ascomycetes it is the terminal cell of a dikaryotic hypha in which

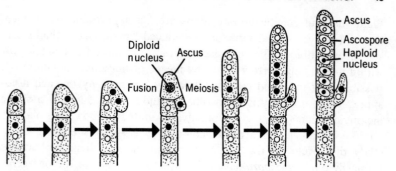

Fig. 3-11. *Ascus and ascospore development.*

nuclear fusion, meiosis, and spore development occur. This developmental sequence is shown in Fig. 3-11. It should be noted that meiosis immediately follows nuclear fusion; the true diploid stage is very short. Meiosis results in the formation of four haploid nuclei. In most cases, each haploid nucleus then undergoes one mitotic division, forming eight nuclei in each ascus. Cleavage of cytoplasm around each nucleus is followed by deposition of a rigid wall, forming a total of eight spores per ascus. In recognition of the manner and place of formation, these spores are called ascospores.

Ascospores, to be effective in dissemination of the fungus to new areas, must be discharged from the fruiting body. Discharge may be passive, or, as in the case of most Ascomycetes, active. Active discharge results in the forcible ejection of the ascospores from the ascus. Cytoplasm excluded from spores during ascospore formation is usually involved in active spore discharge. The interested student is encouraged to read a small book by C. T. Ingold, a delightfully written book on spore-dispersal mechanisms in fungi (see Suggestions for Further Reading).

Of the several Ascomycetes that are important research organisms, the pink bread mold *Neurospora* is worthy of special mention because of its prominence in genetic and biochemical investigations. The developmental cycle of this fungus is essentially similar to that given above; it is mycelial, forms conidia, and produces asci within perithecia as a result of sexual reproduction. Its main vegetative phase is haploid; thus any gene mutation is immediately expressed, and its short generation time speeds genetic investigations. *Neurospora* grows readily on a chemically defined medium; therefore biochemical mutants, easily induced by X-radiation, are simply characterized.

Plants used in genetic investigations are hermaphroditic but hetero-thallic (that is, sexual structures produced on the same thallus are self-incompatible). The eight ascospores are produced in a single row within a relatively narrow ascus; by means of micromanipulation it is possible to isolate and culture separately the progeny of each asco-spore. Thus, not only is it possible to study all products of a single meiotic division (which is not possible in animals or flowering plants), but the linear spatial arrangement of the ascospores enables us to study the results of the first and second meiotic divisions. Studies primarily on *Neurospora* have led to the formulation of the one-gene, one-enzyme concept in biochemical genetics.

Whereas *Neurospora* may be considered a "typical" Ascomycete, there are some, such as brewer's yeast (*Saccharomyces cerevisiae*), that are nonmycelial and lack a fruiting body. In brewer's yeast, the individual cells themselves are transformed into asci and produce ascospores under appropriate conditions. In addition, this and many other yeasts form new cells in a manner unlike most other plants, by a process termed *budding*. New cells arise by the origin and develop-ment of a small bleb on one side of the parent cell (Fig. 3-12). Nu-

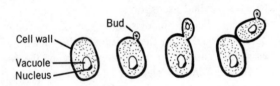

Fig. 3-12. Budding of yeast cells.

clear division occurs and one nucleus moves into the enlarging bud. The bud is ultimately cut off from the mother cell and the two cells separate.

Many studies have been directed toward understanding the me-chanics of budding in yeasts. Time-lapse motion picture studies have shown that buds are initiated by a sudden extrusion of naked proto-plasm through a hole in the yeast cell wall. In contrast to enzymati-cally induced naked protoplasts (discussed earlier with bacterial cell walls), which are unable to synthesize new cell walls, bud proto-plasts are quickly covered by wall material. It is pertinent to note that wall synthesis begins adjacent to the wall of the mother cell, indi-cating the need for a "primer" of pre-existing wall substance for wall synthesis. It has been found that a specific area of the yeast cell is involved in bud initiation (see Nickerson in Suggestions for Further Reading). There appears to be a localized softening of the wall in this area followed by a protoplasmic blowout. Use of radioactive compounds has shown that bud-forming areas are high in sulfhydral groups (–SH), and wall softening is interpreted as resulting from enzymatic reduction of disulfide bonds (–S–S–) to form sulfhydral groups. Results from numerous studies on yeast budding and on mold-yeast dimorphism (described previously) have led to the suggestion that hyphal branching and yeast budding are different morphological manifestations of similar underlying physiological processes.

BASIDIOMYCETES

Basidiomycetes are the fungi most commonly seen in fields and forests and along wooded streams. They include the mushrooms, toadstools, puffballs, and bracket or shelf fungi. Many of these are saprobic or mycorrhizal fungi. This group also includes the rusts and smuts, which are obligate parasites on many vital economic plants.

Basidiomycetes have many points of similarity with the Ascomycetes. Both generally are mycelial, with central pores in the hyphal septa. However, whereas the Ascomycetes have monokaryotic vegetative hyphae, Basidiomycetes have vegetative mycelia usually composed of dikaryotic, functionally diploid hyphae. Hyphal differentiation into asexual reproductive structures, including conidia, is generally similar to that in Ascomycetes, although many Basidiomycetes appear to have lost the capacity for asexual reproduction.

The basidium, generally a club-shaped structure, is the definitive characteristic of Basidiomycetes. Like the ascus, the basidium is a cell in which nuclear fusion and meiosis occurs. However, the spores of the basidium are formed externally, outside of the basidium proper (Fig. 3-13). After meiosis, the haploid nuclei migrate out into each of four small blebs on the distal end of the basidium. Upon enlargement, these blebs mature into spores called *basidiospores*. Two types of basidia are found in the Basidiomycetes: (1) unicellular and (2) septate. Basidia of mushrooms, puffballs, and bracket fungi are unicellular; those of rusts and smuts are septate. The development of a mushroom and a rust is discussed below.

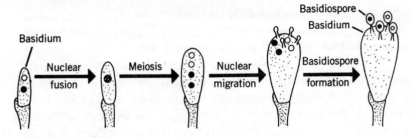

Fig. 3-13. *Basidium and basidiospore development.*

Mushrooms

The term *mushroom* usually refers only to edible Basidiomycetes that have a fruiting body differentiated into cap, stipe, and gills (Fig. 3-14). *Toadstool* usually refers to morphologically similar but

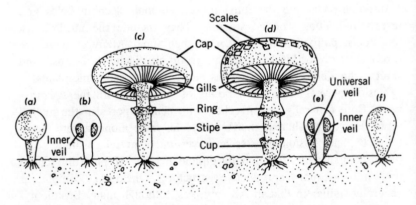

Fig. 3-14. *Fruiting bodies of mushrooms. (a–c) Agaricus type: (a) button stage; (b) section through button; (c) mature fruiting body. (d–f) Amanita type: (d) button stage; (e) section through button; (f) mature fruiting body.*

inedible varieties. It should be emphasized that there is no dividing line between these two groups, because a fungus that is poisonous to one person may be eaten by another with no ill effects. In addition, many edible mushrooms are closely related to poisonous ones. Therefore, mushrooms as discussed in this book include both poisonous and nonpoisonous forms.

As previously mentioned, the main vegetative phase of growth of Basidiomycetes is by dikaryotic hyphae. In contrast to many Ascomycetes, there are no morphologically differentiated sex organs. Dikaryotic hyphae are often established by hyphal fusions between different strains (plus and minus) in heterothallic forms. (There are several other ways, not discussed here, in which a dikaryon may be established in mushrooms.) Once formed, the dikaryon usually is long-lived, living from one to many years, but because it grows within the substrate it is seldom seen. Periodically (in the spring for some fungi and in the late summer or fall for others), fruiting bodies are initiated. As yet, little is known about the physiological changes occurring within the hyphae during the initiation of the reproductive phase.

Fruiting-body initiation of a mushroom results when localized areas of hyphal growth enlarge to form a mass of compacted hyphae referred to as a "button" (see Fig. 3-14a, b). Subsequent enlargement of the button stage, primarily by water uptake, results in the formation of the mature fruiting body. Basidia line both surfaces of the gills and forcibly discharge the basidiospores when mature. Subsequent spore dispersal normally is by wind currents. It is evident that the greater the surface growth of the vegetative mycelium within the substrate, with its greater potential food reserve, the larger the number of mushrooms initiated. In comparison with the Ascomycetes, in which a single sexual act normally results in the formation of a single fruiting body, we find that a single sexual act in mushrooms (and other Basidiomycetes) yields many fruiting bodies.

The origin and development of mushrooms and of other types of fruiting bodies include morphogenetic processes that we are just beginning to understand. The fruiting body is composed of a multitude of individual hyphae. What controls and integrates their growth rate so that the characteristic form and structure of the fruiting body invariably results? Although not completely understood, it has long been recognized that light often has a formative effect. In total darkness there is no development of the cap. Moreover, it has been found that the presence of gills greatly promotes expansion of the cap in one mushroom. The possible involvement of hormones in regulation of growth and development of mushroom fruiting bodies awaits further study.

Some mushrooms, such as the poisonous *Amanita,* possess an additional structure. The immature fruiting body of these mushrooms is enclosed by a thin membrane called a *universal veil* (see Fig. 3-14d–f). Remnants of this veil often remain as scales on the cap and as a basal cup on the mature mushroom. However, presence of scales or of a cup does not automatically designate a poisonous mushroom, since some having the universal veil are edible, while many poisonous mushrooms lack it.

The fruiting bodies of puffballs, which are edible before spore formation, originate like mushrooms. They differ structurally in that the basidia and basidiospores remain enclosed at maturity. Various methods have evolved to ensure adequate spore dispersal. In some puffballs—such as the giant puffball *Calvatia,* which may measure over 45 centimeters in diameter—the outer layer disintegrates and the spores are passively dispersed by the wind. Other puffballs have a fruiting body with an apical pore, which functions like a small bellows when hit by a drop of rain, puffing out clouds of spores that are then wind-dispersed. Perhaps the most elaborate spore-discharge mechanism in this group belongs to *Sphaerobolus* (literally, "sphere thrower"). In this fungus, discharge is effected by the catapulting of the entire spore mass (about 2 mm in diameter) to a distance of about 5 meters (for details, see Ingold in Suggestions for Further Reading).

Rusts

Rusts differ from mushrooms, puffballs, and bracket fungi in two important respects: they have septate basidia, and their basidia are not produced in a fruiting body. Rusts are all obligate plant parasites, and they attack many of man's economic plants, including the cereal grains. Many rusts require two different hosts to complete their normal development; they may produce five separate types of spores during their development. It is not surprising, then, to find that there is an elaborate terminology associated with rusts; a knowledge of this terminology is prerequisite to an understanding of the development and biology of rusts. Probably the most important rust to man is *Puccinia graminis,* which causes the black stem rust of wheat. Wheat is, of course, the basis of Western civilization. Our greatest competitor for wheat, as well as for several other cereal grains, is *Puccinia graminis* and its various strains. The wheat rust is found everywhere that wheat is grown, and is a continual source of economic loss for the wheat grower. The fungus destroys chlorophyll and uses the sugars synthesized by the wheat, resulting in a smaller-than-normal grain size and reduced grain yield per acre. Because of its direct influence on our economy, the life history of the wheat rust is discussed here in detail (see Fig. 3-15).

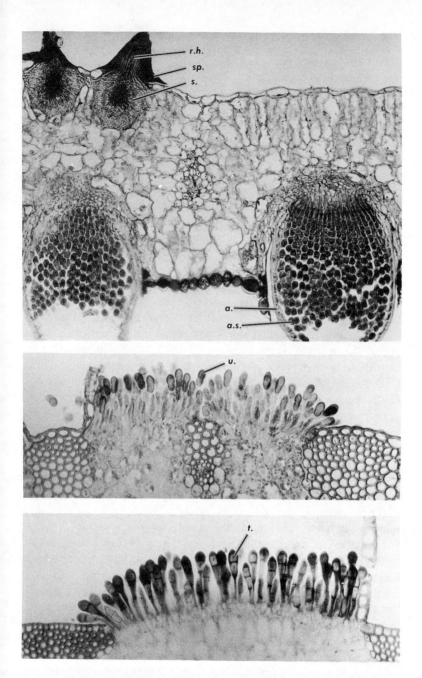

Fig. 3-15. *Puccinia graminis. (a) Spermagonia and aecia on barberry leaf;* s.: *spermagonium;* sp.: *spermatia;* r.h.: *receptive hyphae;* a.: *aecium;* a.s.: *aeciospore. (b) Uredospore formation on wheat; note destruction of host tissue;* u.: *uredospore. (c) Teliospore formation on wheat;* t.: *teliospore (two-celled).*

Perhaps the best place to begin such a discussion is with the uninucleate, haploid basidiospore. The basidiospore is formed during the spring and infects another host of the wheat rust, the common barberry. (This is not to be confused with the Japanese barberry, a commonly cultivated and nonsusceptible ornamental shrub.) Basidiospore germination results in the formation of monokaryotic hyphae, which soon form a small pustule, termed *spermagonium,* on the upper surface of the barberry leaf (Fig. 3-15a). Since the wheat rust is hermaphroditic but heterothallic, basidiospores are of plus and minus types, and resulting spermagonia will be either plus or minus. In addition to forming spermagonia, hyphae grow toward the lower leaf surface and form structures called *aecia primordia.* Aecia primordia, which are initially monokaryotic, do not develop further until they become dikaryotic.

Establishment of the dikaryon is the function of the spermagonium. Within the cavity of a spermagonium, small cells called spermatia bud off, much like conidia, from short hyphal branches. In addition, several long hyphae, called receptive hyphae, extend out of the opening of the spermagonium (see Fig. 3-15a). At maturity, spermatia extrude from the spermagonium in a drop of a sugar-water solution. Flies are commonly attracted to the sugary drop of liquid, and their movements may result in the transfer of a plus spermatium to the receptive hypha of a minus spermagonium; or the reverse may result. Fusion of the spermatium with the receptive hypha is followed by migration of the spermatial nucleus into the receptive hypha, and, presumably, through the hyphae to the aecia primordium. Unfortunately, the details of nuclear migration are not yet clear. It is known that the cells of the aecium become dikaryotic and that aeciospores, which are dikaryotic, bud off in chains. Aeciospores are unable to reinfect the barberry; they can infect only the wheat plant.

Formation of spermagonia and aecia is quite rapid and, by late spring, airborne aeciospores begin to infect the wheat. Upon contact, aeciospores germinate and dikaryotic hyphae penetrate and grow within the wheat plant. Soon, localized areas of hyphal growth rupture the host epidermis, and another type of spore, the *uredospore,* is formed at the tips of short hyphal branches (Fig. 3-15b). The brownish-red coloration of the uredospores, which are dikaryotic, gives the characteristic rust color to this stage of infection. Uredospores, continuously produced during summer, cause a rapid population buildup in a short time period and carry the fungus to new areas. The spores are light and well adapted for airborne dispersal. Toward fall, hyphal metabolism changes to produce a new kind of spore, the *teliospore* (Fig. 3-15c). These spores are formed either in the same lesions that earlier produced uredospores, or in new lesions. Teliospores are black, and their presence has resulted in the common name "black stem rust of wheat" for this fungus. These two-celled spores are thick-walled, resistant structures that function for the survival of the fungus during winter. Teliospores are particularly important in the northern wheat-growing regions, where the winters may be quite invigorating. During the early spring, teliospores germinate; each cell gives rise to a short hyphal branch, the basidium (Fig. 3-16). The basidium soon

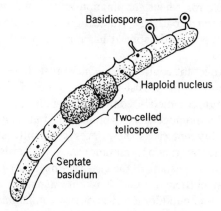

Basidiospore

Haploid nucleus

Two-celled teliospore

Septate basidium

Fig. 3-16. *Basidium and basidiospore development in the rust Gymnosporangium.*

becomes septate, and each cell produces a single, haploid basidiospore. Subsequent basidiospore discharge and barberry infection repeats the life cycle of the wheat rust.

Puccinia graminis is a remarkable organism. Not only does it re-quire two hosts for normal development, but it produces five spore types, each with a different function, within a life span of one year. (The adaptation to two different hosts is not unique in biology. For example, the malarial parasite spends part of its life in man and part of its life in the female mosquito.) Clearly the understanding of the life history of parasitic organisms such as the wheat rust is of prime importance to pathologists, because it often enables them to suggest efficient control measures. In the case of the wheat rust, the suggested answer was to eradicate the common barberry, since it is economically unimportant. A considerable amount of money and energy has been expended toward this goal, and there has been significant success in reducing the amount of annual crop loss. On the other hand, complete control has not been achieved. Why not? The answer comes from understanding the biology of the rust over its entire range in North America. Barberry eradication, which broke the normal developmental cycle of the fungus, did not completely control rust infestation because in the southern limits of the wheat belt (in the southern United States and in Mexico) winters are mild enough to permit the survival of the rust in the uredospore stage. Consequently, these areas serve as reservoirs for infection; uredospores are blown progressively northward during spring and summer as temperatures become favorable for wheat germination and growth in the northern areas. Thus, although barberry eradication has cut down the magnitude of annual loss considerably, it has not completely controlled the wheat rust.

Recent attempts to control the wheat rust have been through genetics, by the breeding of rust-resistant strains of wheat. However, the rust is still not completely controlled. Significantly, wheat rust is not a genetically homogeneous population, but consists of many physiologically different races; new races constantly arise by sexual reproduction and by random mutations. A rust-resistant strain of wheat is one that is resistant to the race of wheat rust *predominant* in one area at that particular time. It is only a matter of time before there is a population buildup of a race of rust compatible with the new strain of wheat. At this time, a new "rust-resistant" strain of wheat must be made available to the farmer. This is the present situation, a never ending fight to stay at least one strain of wheat ahead of the wheat rust. This is also an excellent argument in support of agricultural experiment stations and agriculture-oriented colleges.

SUMMARY

Group	Flagella	Place of meiosis
Chytridiomycetes	One posterior whiplash	Resistant meiosporangium or zygospore
Oömycetes	One whiplash and one tinsel	Antheridium and oögonium (?)
Zygomycetes	None	Coenozygote
Ascomycetes	None	Ascus
Basidiomycetes	None	Basidium

Additional: eucaryotic cellular structure; nonphotosynthetic and heterotrophic.

RELATIONSHIPS

There are at least four theories on the origin of fungi: (1) fungi evolved from certain filamentous bacteria; (2) fungi evolved from certain algae with the loss of photosynthetic pigments; (3) fungi evolved from certain protozoa; and (4) fungi evolved independently from bacteria, algae, and protozoa and are neither plants nor animals —they are fungi and represent a third kingdom of organisms. It is not possible here to discuss these theories in great detail. The following comments, however, are pertinent to an understanding of fungal relationships.

With the emphasis in recent years on flagellation as an important phylogenetic criterion, the fungi formerly placed in the class Phycomycetes were separated into six more or less distinct groups and each group was given a class name. Three of these classes (Chytridiomycetes, Oömycetes, and Zygomycetes) are discussed in this volume.

The presence of a single, posterior whiplash flagellum in members of the class Chytridiomycetes isolates these fungi from other fungi and from most other organisms. This flagellar orientation is not characteristic of any algal group, although it is known to occur in one genus of green algae. The Chytridiomycetes appear to be a phylogenetically distinct group and perhaps should be placed in a separate division.

The Oömycetes characteristically have two flagella, one of the whiplash and one of the tinsel type. In this characteristic, Oömycetes are similar to both brown and chrysophycean algae. Considering other characteristics, the chrysophycean algae appear to be a more promising group and it is possible that the Oömycetes evolved from early chrysophycean stock. This theory is briefly mentioned again in Chapter 8.

The Zygomycetes, predominantly terrestrial fungi, lack flagellated stages in their life histories. Some students of fungi have suggested that Zygomycetes evolved from certain Oömycetes. Although *Saprolegnia* (described earlier) is aquatic, several other members of the Oömycetes illustrate partial to complete adaptation to terrestrial life. Spores of *Phytophthora infestans* and *Plasmopara viticola,* for example, germinate by means of zoospores or germ tubes, depending on environmental conditions. Moreover, spores of the related genus

Peronospora always germinate by means of germ tubes; free water is not necessary for spore germination. It is still not settled, however, whether the Zygomycetes represent the culmination of this aquatic to terrestrial series found in the Oömycetes.

There have been three general theories advanced to explain the origin of Ascomycetes. First, some have suggested that Ascomycetes evolved from certain filamentous bacteria (the Actinomycetes) that produce conidia-like spores. However, the great difference in cellular structure (procaryotic versus eucaryotic) argues against a close, if any, relationship.

A second theory is that Ascomycetes evolved from certain red algae by the loss of photosynthetic pigments. In these two plant groups, the form of the reproductive structures and several details of the processes involved in sexual reproduction appear to be similar. Moreover, the thallus of red algae is basically filamentous, like that of Ascomycetes, and the cells of the filaments are also connected by pores in the cell walls (termed *pits* in the red algae).

A third theory is that Ascomycetes evolved from certain Zygomycetes. In one of the small groups of Zygomycetes (the Endogonaceae) not discussed in this volume, the sexual reproductive structures become surrounded by an envestment of sterile hyphae, forming a fruiting body. Some mycologists think that the Ascomycetes might have evolved from similar zygomycetous fungi.

Basidiomycetes and Ascomycetes show a considerable amount of similarity during the development of the basidium and basidiospores and the ascus and ascospores. Conidia are also present in both groups. These similarities have led many mycologists to suggest that the Basidiomycetes evolved from the Ascomycetes.

The view favored by this author is that the division Eumycota is an unnatural group. The Zygomycetes, Ascomycetes, and Basidiomycetes appear to be genetically related. The relationships of the Oömycetes and the Chytridiomycetes, however, still need clarification.

4

SLIME MOLDS

Slime molds or Myxomycota (myxa = slime) form a small group having practically no economic importance. Nonetheless, slime molds are of considerable interest to biologists because their vegetative phase of growth is animal-like while their reproductive phase is plant-like. They have also been very useful as experimental organisms, and are studied by both botanists and zoologists. Slime molds are common organisms of damp woods, where they may be found by stripping bark off fallen, partially rotted logs. They may also be found in soil, gardens, and lawns. Because of their small size and unique form of vegetative growth, they are not usually noticed.

Slime molds are often separated into two main groups. In one group, called the *cellular* slime molds, the vegetative phase consists of uninucleate, nonflagellated, free-living cells. Organisms in the second group are known as the *true* slime molds. In these, the vegetative stage consists of a multinucleate mass of protoplasm resulting from the fusion of individual cells. Only the true slime molds are discussed below. (Information about cellular slime molds, an important group of research organisms, can be found in the article by Bonner listed in Suggestions for Further Reading.)

CHARACTERISTICS

The main vegetative phase of true slime molds consists of a multinucleate mass of protoplasm called a *plasmodium* (Fig. 4-1). It is from the general appearance of the plasmodium that the name "slime mold" originated. As the plasmodium moves slowly over the substrate, it engulfs and ingests solid food particles such as bacteria, yeast, and fungal spores. Nuclear division is essentially synchronous; that is, all nuclei in a plasmodium undergo division at the same time. As nuclei enter prophase in *Physarum polycephalum,* the plasmodium stops locomotion and contracts slightly. Locomotion resumes im-

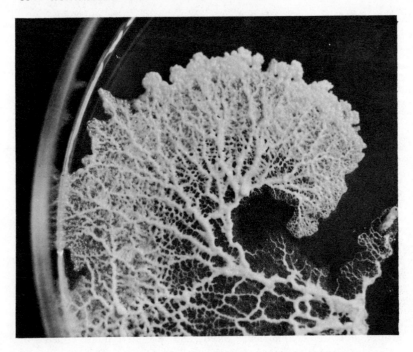

Fig. 4-1. *Plasmodium of Physarum gyrosum in agar culture. Note the interconnected system of tubules. Courtesy of C. J. Alexopoulos, University of Texas. Reproduced by permission.*

mediately at telophase. The nuclear membrane in slime molds persists during nuclear division. Future studies with the electron microscope should clarify the details of stages in nuclear division.

The plasmodium of many slime molds is white; others may contain yellow, orange, or red pigments. Functions of these pigments are poorly understood. They are not photosynthetic. One suggestion is that yellow (and presumably other) pigmented types are more resistant to radiation than are unpigmented ones.

The plasmodium of slime molds lacks any type of a rigid wall. At the front end, where the plasmodium continually comes in contact with new substrate, the undifferentiated protoplasm is separated from the external environment by only a very thin membrane. In older parts of the plasmodium, the protoplasm is differentiated into an interconnected system of tubules that contain streaming cytoplasm. The tubules apparently are protoplasmic in nature and are capable of contraction and expansion. Cytoplasmic streaming in the tubules is easy to observe; for this reason, slime molds have often been studied by elementary students. It is somewhat startling to observe, within a single tubule, two moving masses of cytoplasm flowing in opposite directions at the same time without any apparent membrane separating them. What is the cause of cytoplasmic streaming? We do not yet know for certain. A contractile protein, myxomyosin, similar to the contractile protein actomyosin of animal muscle, has been isolated from slime-mold plasmodia. This protein contracts when the high-energy phosphate compound ATP is added, and it has been suggested that periodic contraction of myxomyosin causes cytoplasm to be moved passively through the tubules.

Under alternating day-night conditions, plasmodial growth continues as long as an adequate food supply and moisture are available. When either of these two factors limits growth, there is a rapid formation of reproductive structures. Experiments have shown that in *Physarum polycephalum* and many other slime molds, light (especially the shorter wavelengths) is necessary for initiation of reproduction; dark-grown plasmodia do not form reproductive structures.

Reproductive structures of slime molds are referred to as fruiting bodies, of which the most common type is the sporangium (Fig. 4-2a, b). During sporangial formation, the plasmodium separates

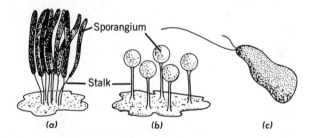

Fig. 4-2. (*a*) *Sporangia of Stemonitis.* (*b*) *Sporangia of Physarum.* (*c*) *Biflagellate swarmer of slime molds.*

into many small mounds of protoplasm, each of which develops into a mature sporangium borne at the tip of a short stalk. During later stages in sporangium maturation, cleavage of the multinucleate protoplasm results in the formation of uninucleate spores. Each spore then develops a rigid wall. Judging from available evidence, meiosis occurs shortly before spore formation. Spores of slime molds, then, may have two important functions: they provide for the survival of the organism during periods unfavorable for vegetative growth, and they may contain new gene combinations resulting from segregation of genetic factors during meiosis.

At maturity, the surface layer of the sporangium flakes off, exposing the spore mass. Filamentous strands, which may help regulate spore dispersal, are usually intermixed with the spores. Spores are small and light and are blown about by the wind. Under favorable conditions, spores germinate and give rise to uninucleate flagellated cells. Usually, two whiplash flagella of unequal length are on the anterior end of each cell (Fig. 4-2c). These cells divide by mitotic divisions to form additional flagellated cells. Sometimes cells lose their flagella and move about like amoebae. Ultimately, two flagellated or nonflagellated cells fuse (*syngamy*) to initiate the plasmodium. Subsequent plasmodial growth occurs mainly by cytoplasmic synthesis and concomitant nuclear divisions. During movement across the substrate, it is possible for a plasmodium to separate into several smaller ones, each capable of continued growth and reproduction. It is also possible for individual plasmodia of the same species to fuse with each other.

This account of slime-mold development, although serving as a general introduction to these organisms, does not introduce the student to the many interesting unsolved problems in this group. For example, one of the most important aspects in slime-mold development is the apparent absolute dependency of plasmodium formation on cell fusion. In 1958 it was found that the addition of chelating agents to cultures of young flagellated cells inhibited both cell fusion and plasmodium formation. The flagellated cells continued to divide as long as food (bacteria) was available, but they did not fuse. Only when these cells were transferred to a medium lacking chelating agents were plasmodia initiated. We still do not know the specific role of these agents: what metal ions are being chelated or how the plasma membrane is altered. The mechanism by which cell fusion triggers plasmodium formation, and what biochemical differences exist between the free-living cells and the plasmodium, are other critical questions.

The vegetative plasmodial phase containing synchronously dividing nuclei has made the slime molds excellent organisms for cytological and biochemical research. It is now possible to grow *Physarum polycephalum* in a chemically defined liquid medium. In addition, complete separation of vegetative growth from reproduction is under control of the investigator. Moreover, the large plasmodial size makes possible the sequential sampling of protoplasm during studies of biochemical changes correlated with morphological changes during sporulation. Removal of bits of protoplasm does not at all affect the metabolism of the rest of the plasmodium. Synchronous nuclear divisions also make possible the analysis of protein and nucleic acid synthesis, enzymatic changes, and other events during various stages of the nuclear-division cycle.

SUMMARY

Flagella

One or two whiplash, anterior insertion

Vegetative growth

Plasmodial

Additional: eucaryotic cellular structure; diploid vegetative phase; haploid resting meiospores.

RELATIONSHIPS

The slime molds, with their plasmodial vegetative phase and spore-producing reproductive phase, form a distinct group of organisms. They have several attributes (including flagellar details) in common with one group of organisms often classified as fungi (the Plasmodiophoromycetes, a class not discussed in this volume). However, some researchers, including this author, think that the Plasmodiophoromycetes should be classified with the slime molds since they appear to have more in common with slime molds than they do with fungi.

The slime molds are also placed with the protozoa in the animal kingdom, where they are classified with the amoeboid (rhizopod) organisms. The slime molds appear to be highly evolved plasmodial organisms. Some rather good arguments have been advanced in support of the view that slime molds evolved from amoeboid protozoa-like ancestors. On the other hand, many of the amoeboid protozoa appear to have evolved from certain photosynthetic chrysophycean-like ancestors, considered to be algae by botanists. It seems best to keep the slime molds in a separate division, the Myxomycota, until more information becomes available and until problems in protozoan and algal phylogeny have been resolved.

5

INTRODUCTION

TO ALGAE

Although the term "algae" does not enjoy formal taxonomic recognition, it is in wide general use and is familiar to most people. Basically, algae are photosynthetic, nonembryo-producing plants. (An embryo is here considered as a multicellular young plant produced from the zygote and developed within the female reproductive structure.) As indicated in Chapter 1, algae do not form a natural group but are subdivided into several divisions. It is of interest to note that common names of most algal divisions refer to a color, such as red, green, blue-green, or brown. This color is characteristic of algae within a division and is due to the presence and different proportions of pigments in the cells.

Most algae are aquatic plants; they are the grass of the waters. The majority of free-floating and attached plants of both salt and fresh water are algae, and they may be abundant enough to color the water. The Red Sea reputedly derived its name from the occasional tremendous growths of a microscopic red-colored alga (which is a member of the blue-green algae division). Many others are soil algae and grow either in or on the surface of damp soil, where they are subjected to periodic drying. Relatively few algae are capable of surviving as epiphytes on the trunks and branches of trees. But the truly subaerial algae are able to survive rapid temperature fluctuations, temperature extremes, and long periods of dryness.

Although most algae are free-living, some occur in symbiotic associations with other organisms. Lichens—associations of fungi with either green or blue-green algae—have already been described. Some algae also live in close association with animals. One species of *Paramecium* (a unicellular protozoan) contains in its cytoplasm photosynthetic cells of a green alga; another green alga grows within the tissue of certain *Hydra* (a coelenterate). A few algae are even parasitic. Certain flowering plants are parasitized by green algae and a few red algae are parasitic on close red algal relatives.

Since algae are predominantly aquatic plants, they are found in practically all bodies of water used by man, where they are often troublesome. Many communities obtain water from rivers, streams, lakes, ponds, or reservoirs, and algal growths in these bodies of water, and in swimming pools, may become extremely rapid at certain times of the year, producing "algal blooms." Not only do many of these algae impart fishy, musty, septic, grassy, or other disagreeable odors to our drinking water, but they may clog filters of water filtration plants. In smaller bodies of water, copper sulfate is often added to control algal growth, but concentrations needed to kill all undesirable algae also kill other forms of aquatic life. In addition, it is usually not desirable to kill all algae in water, because they help keep water aerobic and tend to reduce water hardness. An area of current research is in the synthesis and application of selective algicides—chemical compounds that may be used to inhibit growth of specific undesirable algae in bodies of water.

On the other hand, growths of large quantities of algae in sewage-disposal ponds has been encouraged. For many years, sanitary engineers have observed massive growths of green algae such as species of *Chlorella, Chlamydomonas,* and *Scenedesmus* (Fig. 5-1), in addition to bacteria, in sewage-treatment tanks and filter beds. Only after extensive research has the relationship that exists between these sewage algae and bacteria become apparent. It has been found that

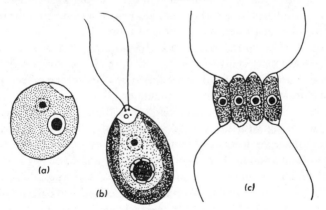

Fig. 5-1. *Common algae of sewage-treatment tanks.* (*a*) *Chlorella.* (*b*) *Chlamydomonas.* (*c*) *Scenedesmus.*

aerobic bacterial breakdown products of sewage are also primary photosynthetic requirements for these algae. Also, oxygen produced by algae can be an effective and inexpensive means of meeting the oxygen needs of aerobic sewage bacteria and thus prevent putrefaction. This relationship existing between algae and bacteria in a small sewage-treatment tank is summarized in Fig. 5-2. Slightly acidic raw

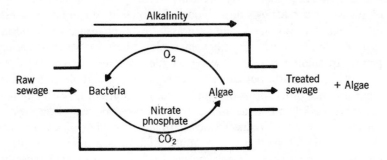

Fig. 5-2. *Algal-bacterial interrelationship in a sewage-treatment tank.*

sewage enters the pond at one end and is immediately acted upon by bacteria. The large amount of organic matter supports a very large bacterial population in this region of the pond, and sewage breakdown is rapid. Sewage input is a continuous process and, as the partially treated sewage moves slowly through the pond, the algal population, initially small, increases in number. As the algae utilize the nitrates, phosphates, and carbon dioxide (made available by bacterial activity), the sewage becomes more and more alkaline. This alkaline condition inhibits most sewage bacteria so that in the discharged, treated sewage there is a very low bacterial population and a very high algal one. Various modifications of this type of pond have been used in sewage treatment in several communities.

The large number of nutrients tied up in the algal protoplasts are discharged along with the treated sewage-pond effluent. Several investigators have been interested in the possibility of harvesting these algae for animal food. Major problems confronting these workers are those of finding techniques to harvest the algae and to establish suitable algae in sewage ponds. A similar but closed ecological system is under investigation for possible use in space travel. The result of algal and bacterial interaction under controlled conditions may solve the problems of sewage disposal, air rejuvenation, and water recycling during long-range space explorations. Algae, in turn, could be harvested periodically and used as food.

A considerable amount of research also has been directed toward the mass culturing of algae to meet future food needs of man. In terms of available space for plant culture, the physical resources of our planet are drastically limiting; it is known that on a dry-weight basis algal culture makes a more efficient utilization of space than either crop plants or meat animals. Much of the research has been done on various strains of the green alga *Chlorella* (see Fig. 5-1a). These strains differ in their growth rates and nutritional value, such as in proportions of carbohydrates, fats, and proteins in the cells.

Algae have also been important organisms in research on photosynthetic processes. For example, much of our knowledge regarding the pathway of carbon during photosynthesis has been obtained from studies on algae, primarily green algae. The importance of photosynthesis cannot be overemphasized. Photosynthesis not only results in the liberation of molecular oxygen, which is essential for aerobic respiration, but it also is the most efficient system known in which radiant energy is converted to chemical energy. Although the pathway of carbon during photosynthesis is now quite well known, we still have much to learn about the energy-trapping mechanism itself—as, for example, how radiant energy from the sun is trapped by chlorophyll and other pigment molecules in chloroplasts, and how electrons are transferred from molecule to molecule during this and other cellular processes. Algae (and photosynthetic bacteria as well) will no doubt continue to be important research organisms in these studies. Current and future research in the area of energy-trapping and electron-transfer systems is at the level of submolecular biology. Needless to say, the influence of chemistry and physics on this level of biological research has been tremendous. But we must not lose sight of the fact that biology is more than a series of test-tube reactions, and any information obtained from isolated systems must be put back into its proper biological framework: that of the living, metabolizing cell and organism.

One of the most common overgeneralizations in regard to algae is that because they are photosynthetic, algae require only inorganic compounds—water, carbon dioxide, and light—for growth. While this is true for some, especially green algae, many in addition need one or more specific organic compounds for growth. For example, vitamin B_{12} (which is also needed by animals and humans) is required by many. Actually, the nutritional requirements of few algae have been critically studied, and there are many that we have not yet been able to culture. Although it might seem reasonable to assume that algae cultured in the dark would be able to grow if the medium was supplemented with a sugar normally present in light-grown cells, many algae fail to grow under these conditions. Some of these algae appear to have an obligate requirement for light; why they are unable to utilize any externally supplied carbon source in the dark is an unsolved physiological problem. Additional studies are needed on the basic biochemistry, physiology, and reproduction of more algae.

FORM OF ALGAE

Algae range in size from microscopic, unicellular plants to the highly differentiated, multicellular seaweeds that may be over 60 meters long. Unicellular algae are found in all divisions of algae with only one exception (brown algae), and are considered to be basic cell types from which, through evolution, other forms of body construction developed. Unicellular algae may be propelled through water by means of one or more flagella, or they may be nonflagellated, and they may or may not have a rigid carbohydrate cell wall. Colonial algae are organisms in which daughter cells do not separate. This association may be loose, as in the blue-green alga *Gloeocapsa* (Fig. 5-3a), or integrated, as in the green alga *Volvox* (Fig. 5-3b, c), in which individual cells are interconnected by thin protoplasmic strands. Filamentous algae develop from single cells in which division occurs in a single dimension and in which the resulting filament may be branched or unbranched (Fig. 5-3d, e). Membranous and more complex seaweeds also develop from single cells during their normal development, but cell divisions occur in more than one dimension (Fig. 5-3f, g). A few algae consist of nonseptate, branched, multinucleate tubes. In these algae, nuclear division occurs without accompanying cell division.

There is considerable diversity in form among unicellular and colonial algae. Many of these algae are planktonic organisms and possess flattened cells, cellular processes, or other flotation devices to keep the plants near the water surface, where light intensity is optimal. (Plankton are small, free-living plants and animals readily carried about by currents and found in almost all bodies of water. The

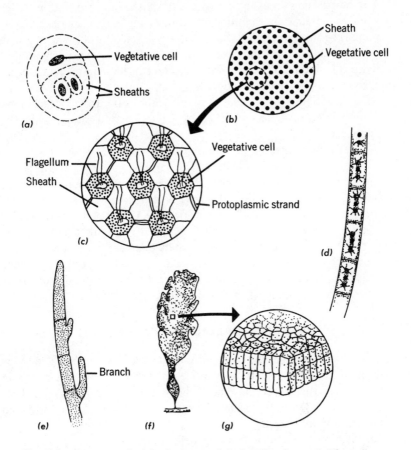

Fig. 5-3. *Common algal body forms. (a) Small colony of Gloeo-capsa (a blue-green alga). (b) Low-power view of a colony of Volvox (a green alga). (c) High-power view of Volvox. (d) Unbranched filament of Zygnema (a green alga). (e) Branched view of Cladophora (a green alga). (f) Habit drawing of Ulva (a green alga). (g) High-power view of a portion of the plant of Ulva.*

plants are referred to as *phytoplankton;* the animals, as *zooplankton.*) Planktonic algae are the beginning point of many food chains. These microscopic plants are eaten by progressively larger organisms, including fish which in turn may be eaten by man.

phytoplankton → zooplankton → small fish → large fish → man

The best fishing areas in the world are those high in plankton. It has been found that the addition of nitrates and other inorganic compounds to small bodies of water that are deficient in these compounds usually results in an increase in both algal growth and fish productivity. Planktonic algae are also important in helping to maintain the carbon dioxide–oxygen ratio of the atmosphere. It has been estimated that about 90 per cent of photosynthesis occurs in oceans; most of this, in turn, is accomplished by phytoplankton, about which we know very little.

Most larger algae are *benthic* forms. That is, they are attached to the bottom in aquatic habitats. The largest and most complex are found in marine waters, where they are common inhabitants of the intertidal zone. (The intertidal zone is defined as that area between the mean high tide and the mean low tide.) Although many benthic algae are eaten by animals such as sea urchins, they are less important in food chains leading to man than are plankton algae. It should be mentioned, however, that culturing and harvesting of certain benthic red and brown marine algae is a flourishing food industry in several Asiatic countries, including China and Japan.

CELLULAR STRUCTURE AND FUNCTION

We have seen that the unicell is considered to be the basic cell type from which other body types have been derived. Although details in form and structure of the unicell differ in each algal division, there are many general similarities. Thus a description of the form and function of the flagellated unicell at this time will also serve as an introduction to the algal cell in general (Fig. 5-4).

Cells of most algae are surrounded by a primarily carbohydrate wall in which cellulose is almost always present. In addition, the walls of many algae contain a gelatinous material that is often pectinaceous. This material has various functions in algae; in colonial forms it holds the cells together, and in many subaerial algae it helps retard desiccation. Other carbohydrates obtained from the cell walls of several marine brown and red algae are of commercial importance and will be described in more detail later.

Motility is due to the activity of one or more (usually two) flagella that are laterally or anteriorly inserted (see Fig. 5-4a). Each flagellum arises from a basal granule within the cytoplasm and extends through a pore in the cell wall to the outside. Characteristically, green algae

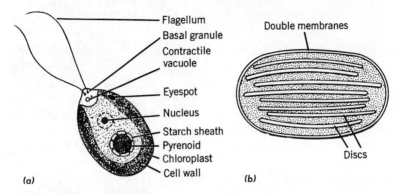

Fig. 5-4. (*a*) *Cell structure of Chlamydomonas* (*a green alga*). (*b*) *Diagrammatic representation of the structure of an algal chloroplast.*

have two whiplash flagella, euglenoids have one (or more) tinsel flagella, and brown algae have one of each type. The flagellum is an organelle for locomotion. Although several different patterns of flagellar motion have been described in algae, we still know little about the biophysics of flagellar contraction, or how impulses are transmitted along the length. Many unicellular algae lack flagella. In some cases this appears to be a derived condition. It is known that mutants of flagellated cells showing a permanent loss of flagella can be induced to arise in the laboratory, and they probably also occur in nature. It is possible that the nonflagellated green alga *Chlorella* evolved from a flagellated ancestor.

Flagellated cells of many algae are capable of reacting to variations in light intensity; they may swim toward or away from a light source, depending on its intensity (positive and negative phototaxis, respectively). In order to react, cells must absorb light. Many flagellated cells possess an eyespot—a modified part of the chloroplast—which contains a red or orange carotenoid pigment (see Fig. 5-4a). The eyespot is involved in the phototactic responses of many algae, but the mechanism of its involvement has been clearly shown in only one organism (*Euglena*).

The chloroplast is a prominent cell organelle. It is a complex structure made up of numerous flattened discs that are separated from the cytoplasm by a double membrane (Fig. 5-4b). In a three-dimensional representation, an individual disc can be roughly compared to a

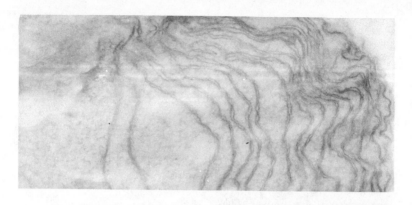

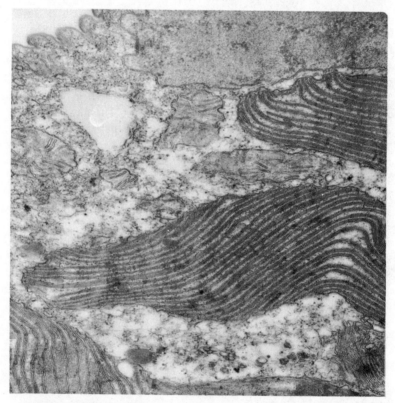

Fig. 5-5. *Ultrastructure of algal chloroplasts. Top: Nemalion (a red alga). Bottom: Euglena gracilis var. bacillaris. Note that the chloroplast discs of Nemalion are single, whereas those of Euglena are arranged in stacks. Bottom photo courtesy of Dr. Sarah P. Gibbs. Reproduced by permission.*

flattened balloon. The disc membranes, positionally comparable to the rubber of the balloon, enclose proteinaceous substances just as air is enclosed in the balloon. Investigations with the electron microscope have shown that the chloroplast structure of red algae (Fig. 5-5, top) differs from that of other algae. The discs occur singly in red algae whereas they are stacked in groups of two or more in other algae (Fig. 5-5, bottom). The chlorophyll and carotenoid pigments are structurally parts of the disc membranes.

Chloroplasts of many algae contain one or more specialized proteinaceous areas called pyrenoids (see Fig. 5-4a). Pyrenoids in green algae are associated with starch synthesis. In these algae, and in other green plants, starch always forms within chloroplasts (or their colorless counterparts). Pyrenoids are found in chloroplasts of many algae in other divisions. In these algae, however, careful studies with the electron microscope have indicated that polysaccharide food reserve is synthesized externally to the chloroplast, sometimes far removed from the vicinity of a pyrenoid. Function of the pyrenoid in these algae is unknown.

In addition, cells of most flagellated fresh-water algae also contain one or more contractile vacuoles that function as osmotic regulators. In fresh water, the concentration of dissolved substances within the cell is higher than in the surrounding water. Consequently, the water that tends to move into the cell is removed by the activity of these vacuoles.

The structure and function of mitochondria and nuclei of algae are similar to those of plants in general and need not be described in detail here. It is sufficient to remember that both of these structures are limited externally by a double membrane.

6

BLUE-GREEN

ALGAE

Blue-green algae or Cyanophyta (cyan = blue) are found in a wide variety of environments. They occur in marine and fresh water, on and in soil, and on wet stones, cement, and plant pots. Some can withstand the temperatures of hot springs, others the cold of arctic pools. Certain blue-green algae such as *Anabaena* are able to utilize elemental nitrogen from the atmosphere to build their proteins, thereby contributing to the nitrogenous content of soil. This process of nitrogen fixation, which is similar to that found in some bacteria, is important to maintain soil fertility such as that needed in rice paddies.

Except for nitrogen fixation, blue-green algae are of little direct importance to man. Some are conspicuous components of algal water blooms and occasionally have been implicated in the illness and death of mammals, waterfowl, fish, and man. Laboratory studies on cultures have shown that a few of the blue-green algae produce toxic compounds. Two factors that can cause death have been described from a species of the nonfilamentous *Microcystis* commonly found in toxic water blooms. One, called a fast-death factor, results in death in one to two hours, preceded by pallor, convulsions, and prostration. The fast-death factor, an endotoxin, is a polypeptide of ten amino acid residues.

GENERAL CHARACTERISTICS

The cellular structure of blue-green algae is relatively simple (Fig. 6-1). These algae have no double-membrane structures such as chloroplasts, nuclei, or mitochondria. Their cellular organization, like that of bacteria, is termed *procaryotic*. Additional studies are

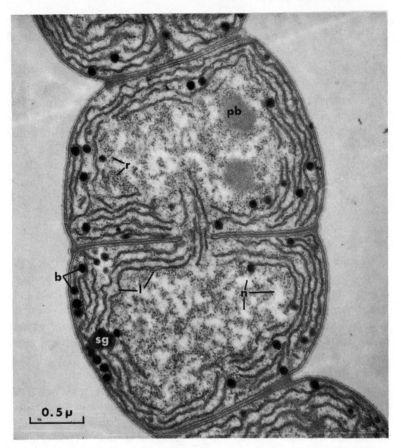

Fig. 6-1. *Electronmicrograph of Nostoc punctiforme. Note the absence of nuclear membranes, chloroplast membranes, and mitochondria. b.: β granules (osmiophilic granules); l.: photosynthetic membranes (chromatophores); n.: nucleoplasm; pb.: polyhedral bodies; sg.: structured granules; r.: ribosomes. Courtesy of Dr. T. E. Jensen and Prof. C. C. Bowen, Iowa State University. Used by permission.*

still needed to determine whether blue-green algae have metabolic pathways similar to those in other algae and higher plants.

Chloroplasts, as discrete bodies, are absent. The photosynthetic pigments are found in numerous flattened photosynthetic membranes (chromatophores) located in the peripheral part of the cell. These photosynthetic membranes are similar to those of photosynthetic bacteria and can be considered structurally and functionally comparable to the discs of a chloroplast. Chlorophyll molecules are a structural component of both the photosynthetic membrane and the chloroplast disc membrane. In blue-green algae, only one kind of chlorophyll, chlorophyll *a,* is found. However, a few other pigments involved in photosynthesis are also present. Two of these are structurally similar to bile pigments of animals. In blue-green algae, these water-soluble bile pigments, called *biliproteins* (or phycobilins), may be either blue (phycocyanin) or red (phycoerythrin). These red and blue biliproteins absorb light in regions of the spectrum different from chlorophyll molecules. Laboratory studies have shown that light energy absorbed by biliproteins participates in photosynthesis, apparently by transferring its absorbed energy to chlorophyll molecules. Excess sugar resulting from photosynthesis is stored as a carbohydrate called cyanophycean starch.

In spite of the name, many blue-green algae may be purple, red, yellow, or green as a result of variations in the kinds and proportions of pigments, particularly of biliproteins. A few are colorless and thus nonphotosynthetic. Although some authors consider the nonpigmented forms to be bacteria, these nonphotosynthetic plants closely resemble certain pigmented blue-green algae in size, form, and manner of motility.

The nuclear material, which is not bounded by a membrane, is generally located in the central region of the cell. DNA is present, but chromosomes have not been identified; a normal mitotic division does not occur. The nuclear material is more or less equally divided during cell division. We do not yet understand how a complete set of genes is equally divided during division. Until 1963, genetic evidence for the existence of sexuality in this algal division had not been found. However, apparent genetic recombination occurs in *Anacystis nidulans,* a colonial blue-green alga. Two strains of this alga were used for this study: one strain was resistant to penicillin but sensitive to streptomycin; the other was sensitive to penicillin but resistant to streptomycin. Cells of these strains were mixed together and cultured in a medium that lacked both antibiotics. Therefore, growth of neither strain was inhibited. Subsequently, inocula were withdrawn and transferred to culture flasks containing both antibiotics. Growth occurred in a significant number of cultures. Since neither strain will grow separately under these conditions, it seems probable that growth resulted from the appearance of recombinant cells resistant to both antibiotics. In these preliminary studies, the number of recombinants was estimated to be one in about 100 million cells of the parental populations. This is in keeping with results obtained during early study on bacterial sexuality. It is probable that sexuality in blue-green algae is similar to that in bacteria (that is, conjugation). Future research will indicate how widespread and important sexuality is in blue-green algae and the type(s) of genetic systems involved.

Cell walls, rigid sheaths, and gelatinous sheaths have been described for many species. Although cellulose, pectic substances, and several other compounds have been reported, the chemical composition, structure, and biosynthesis of cell walls and sheaths of these algae are poorly known. Additional studies utilizing modern techniques are needed to fill this gap in our knowledge.

There are no flagellated cells, either vegetative or reproductive, in blue-green algae, and there is no evidence to indicate that these algae evolved from flagellated ancestors. In this division, the nonflagellated unicell is considered to be the basic cell type. Many blue-green algae such as *Gloeocapsa* (which is common on damp terrestrial habitats like wet rocks or flower pots in greenhouses) are colonial; the individual cells are held together by a gelatinous sheath (Fig. 6-2a). In

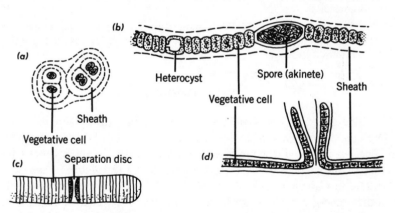

Fig. 6-2. *Representative blue-green algae. (a) Gloeocapsa. (b) Anabaena. (c) Oscillatoria. (d) Scytonema.*

these forms, asexual reproduction occurs simply by fragmentation of the parent colony. However, the commonest body form in this division is the filament, which may be branched or unbranched (Fig. 6-2b–d).

There is usually little cell specialization along the filament. An exception is the separation disc (Fig. 6-2c), resulting from the death of an occasional cell along the filament in *Oscillatoria* and a few others. In *Anabaena* and some other plants, specialized cells called heterocysts are formed (Fig. 6-2b). These two cell types aid vegetative reproduction (fragmentation) by forming weak places along the filament. Relatively few species form resistant spores, which are enlarged vegetative cells filled with food storage material and surrounded by a thick wall. In most blue-green algae, the cytoplasm itself is capable of withstanding long periods of unfavorable conditions.

Although flagellated cells are absent, many species are capable of movement. For example, *Oscillatoria* (Fig. 6-2c) moves by a gliding movement, and attached filaments, which are free at only one end, exhibit a slow, oscillating motion. Recent studies indicate that maximum movement in some blue-green algae is induced by radiation with red or blue-violet light.

SUMMARY

Photosynthetic pigments	Flagella	Food reserve
Chlorophyll *a*	None	Cyanophycean starch
Biliproteins		

Additional: procaryotic cellular organization (no nuclear, mitochondrial, or chloroplast double-membranes); conjugation type of sexual reproduction?; amitosis.

RELATIONSHIPS

Blue-green algae are believed to represent primitive plants that have remained more or less at the evolutionary level at which they arose. There is fossil evidence indicating their antiquity. Filaments that have been compared to those of present-day, living *Oscillatoria* have been found in Canadian rocks at least one and a half billion years old, and other blue-green algal-like forms have been identified in rocks over 500 million years old.

In cellular structure, blue-green algae more nearly resemble bacteria than other algae. It is not surprising, then, that blue-green algae have been postulated as merely advanced bacteria, or, conversely, that bacteria are simplified blue-green algae. These two groups, however, differ in a number of respects, such as types of chlorophyll pigments, details of photosynthesis, presence of flagella, and manner of motility. These differences lead to the conclusion that blue-green algae are not closely related to bacteria, but that these two groups are at the same evolutionary level of organization. Probably they evolved from different ancestors during the same period of geologic time.

7

RED ALGAE

Red algae or Rhodophyta (rhodo = red) are most commonly found along rocky stretches of seacoast. Most of them grow in the lower part of the intertidal zone or in deeper water where they are not exposed to the full force of wave action. Red algae are found in all oceans but are more abundant in warm marine water. Although they are mostly marine, several fresh-water species are known. These usually grow in cold, swift-flowing streams. The fact that most marine red algae are red in color can be used to distinguish them from almost all other algae.

Some red algae are found in coral reefs, and studies on present-day reef formation in the Southern Hemisphere indicate that coralline red algae are more important in reef building than are coral animals. Fossil calcareous reefs give evidence for the existence of red algae as far back as 400 million years ago.

GENERAL CHARACTERISTICS

Red algae are relatively small plants. Most species are less than two feet long, but only a few are microscopic. *Porphyridium* (Fig. 7-1), which is found in both fresh and brackish water and is of obscure relationship to other red algae, is one of the few unicellular species known. Other species vary from delicate membranous sheets (such as *Porphyra*) or simple branched filaments to intricately branched, lacy

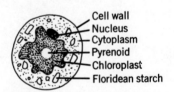

Cell wall
Nucleus
Cytoplasm
Pyrenoid
Chloroplast
Floridean starch

Fig. 7-1. *Cell structure of Porphyridium, a unicellular red alga.*

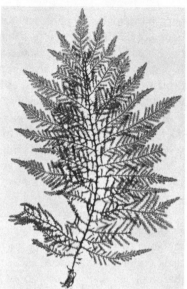

Fig. 7-2. *Photographs of two red algae. Left: Farlowia. Right: Ptilota.*

types (Fig. 7-2). The plant body of many red algae, such as *Nemalion,* is composed of highly branched filaments. In these algae, one or more filaments of elongate cells form the axis of the plant; from these intertwined axial filaments arise numerous, highly branched lateral filaments. The deeply pigmented lateral filaments are the main photosynthetic parts of the plants; the axial filaments are usually colorless.

The cell structure of red algae is eucaryotic. Nuclei, mitochondria, and chloroplasts, all bounded by double membranes, are found. Chlorophyll *a,* the main photosynthetic pigment in algae, is present. Another chlorophyll, chlorophyll *d,* has also been isolated from a few red algae. The characteristic red color of most red algae is due to the abundance of the biliprotein phycoerythrin. The blue biliprotein phycocyanin is also present in many red algae, but usually in smaller amounts. The phycocyanin of red and blue-green algae appears to be identical, whereas phycoerythrin in these two algal groups is not the same.

Many elegant studies on light absorption by nonchlorophyll pigments have been carried out using red algae. These investigations have shown that, as in blue-green algae, light energy absorbed by biliproteins participates in photosynthesis. The presence of biliproteins undoubtedly influences the distribution of marine red algae. Many of these algae grow in deep water or in shaded areas where light intensity is relatively low. Accessory photosynthetic pigments such as biliproteins absorb wavelengths of light not absorbed by chlorophyll, which results in a more efficient utilization of available light energy.

Pyrenoids are present in chloroplasts of some red algae, but they do not appear to be involved in the synthesis of carbohydrate food reserves. Floridean starch, similar to but not identical with starch of flowering plants, is the most common type of food-storage product. It accumulates as small granules outside the chloroplast in the cell cytoplasm.

The cell is surrounded by a wall of two layers. The inner layer, next to the cell membrane, contains cellulose. The outer layer is mucilaginous, which causes the slimy surface of many red algae. It contains colloidal substances and serves to prevent the rapid drying of intertidal red algae when exposed during low tide.

Considerable research is being done on the chemical composition of the cell wall in red algae, because colloidal substances of some red algae have great economic importance. For example, *Gelidium* and a few other genera are the sources of agar, perhaps best known as a culture medium for bacteria and fungi. Agar has a number of additional uses. It has been used in fruit cakes to retain moisture for long periods of time, in icings, frostings, pie fillings, cheeses, mayonnaise, salad dressings, tooth pastes, and shaving creams, and in cosmetics as a base for greaseless creams. Most commercial agar comes from Japan, but red algae have also been harvested for their agar content on the east and west coasts of North America. A few red algal species are also used in soups and as food flavorings, and pieces of *Porphyra,* a common plant of the upper intertidal zone, are used on cookies and crackers and in soups in the Orient.

Sexual reproduction is oögamous, which is considered to be an advanced condition. In contrast to most oögamous algae, red algae have nonflagellated male gametes. In fact, there are no known flagellated cells, either vegetative or reproductive, in this algal division. The vegetative plant of simpler red algae is haploid; the only diploid stage is the zygote. The life history of advanced species is much more complex, often consisting of three separate stages with free-living or parasitic haploid and diploid plants. A detailed discussion of variations in the life histories of these plants is beyond the scope of this book.

It should be mentioned, however, that scientists use details of sexual reproduction for the identification of species of red algae.

SUMMARY

Photosynthetic pigments	Flagella	Food reserve
Chlorophyll *a*	None	Floridean starch
± Chlorophyll *d*		
Biliproteins		

Additional: eucaryotic cellular structure; oögamous sexual reproduction; details of and processes following sexual reproduction usually complex; mostly marine plants.

RELATIONSHIPS

Red algae are a well-defined group. They resemble blue-green algae in being nonflagellated and in having biliproteins. However, not all biliproteins of these two groups are identical, and they are also found in other algae (for example, in members of the Cryptophyceae, a small group of interesting flagellated algae not discussed in this book). With an increasing interest in the study of photosynthetic mechanisms in algae grown in culture, it is possible that we will find biliproteins more widely distributed than now thought. At this time, we must be careful not to place too much weight on their possession of biliproteins as an indication of close relationship.

The eucaryotic cellular structure of red algae can be used to argue against a close relationship between red and blue-green algae. All double-membrane structures present in red algal cells are absent in blue-green algae. This fact indicates a basic difference in the organization of biochemical pathways in these two algal divisions. It is likely that red algae arose directly from nonblue-green algal ancestors. They probably arose in geologic time after the blue-green algae, but from nonflagellated, nucleated ancestors, and at a time when possession of biliproteins was an adaptive advantage to algae. The possible relationship of red algae to the Ascomycetes was discussed in Chapter 3.

8

GOLDEN ALGAE

AND DIATOMS

The division Chrysophyta (chryso = golden) includes unicellular or colonial planktonic algae of marine or fresh water. They play an important role in the economy of nature both as photosynthesizers and as the starting points for many food chains.

Chrysophytes have eucaryotic cellular structures. Chlorophyll *a* is the dominant green pigment, and excess food is stored either as the glucose polymer chrysolaminarin (leucosin), or as oils. In addition, cell walls and walls of resistant spores of many chrysophytes contain silica. The Chrysophyta is separated into three groups: yellow-green algae (Xanthophyceae), golden algae (Chrysophyceae) and diatoms (Bacillariophyceae). Since yellow-green algae and golden algae are essentially similar in form, only the golden algae and diatoms are discussed here.

GOLDEN ALGAE

Golden algae (Chrysophyceae) are predominantly unicellular organisms, although both colonial and filamentous types are known. Unicellular and colonial golden algae are either nonflagellated or flagellated. Flagellated forms generally possess either a single tinsel flagellum or one tinsel and one whiplash flagellum (Fig. 8-1). A rigid cell wall may or may not be present. Forms that lack a wall either may have a definite cell shape or may be amoeboid with radiating cytoplasmic processes called *pseudopodia* (Fig. 8-1c). Moreover, some golden algae have a characteristic shape during certain growth phases and are amoeboid during others. *Chrysamoeba* (Fig. 8-1b) spends much of its life as a flagellated, free-swimming unicell with a definite cell shape. However, it also sends out radiating cytoplasmic processes and becomes amoeboid (Fig. 8-1c). It may even tempo-

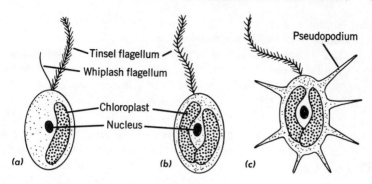

Fig. 8-1. (a) *Ochromonas.* (b) *Chrysamoeba, free-swimming form.* (c) *Chrysamoeba, amoeboid form.*

rarily lose its flagellum. After a period of amoeboid existence, the flagellum reappears and the cell swims away. In both phases, *Chrysamoeba* is photosynthetic. It is of interest that permanent loss of the flagellum in a *Chrysamoeba*-like form would result in the origin of a permanently amoeboid golden alga. Several similar forms exist in nature. Loss of chloroplasts would result in a form similar to those of amoeboid protozoans. Nonphotosynthetic golden algae are also known; these algae resemble pigmented ones in their cellular structure and food reserve.

Reproduction in the golden algae is relatively simple. Asexual reproduction in many of these algae is by means of flagellated mitospores (zoospores). Sexual reproduction appears to be rare; at least it has been observed only infrequently. Many golden algae survive unfavorable conditions by the formation of endogenous cysts within the cells. The walls of these cysts are often highly ornamented and consist of two parts: a silicified "bottle" and a nonsilicified "plug." Upon advent of favorable conditions, the plug is dissolved and the alga emerges.

The color of golden algae is due to the carotenoid pigment fucoxanthin, which masks the green chlorophyll. Fucoxanthin is found in the chloroplasts and, like the chemically unrelated biliproteins of red and blue-green algae, participates in photosynthesis by the transferal of trapped radiant energy to chlorophyll *a*. Even though they are photosynthetic, most if not all golden algae can satisfy their carbon needs by means other than photosynthesis. For example, *Ochromonas* (see Fig. 8-1a) is capable of photosynthesizing all its carbon needs from carbon dioxide when grown in the light (except for vitamins that must be present in the medium). *Ochromonas* can also obtain carbon compounds from the surrounding medium both by diffusion of low-molecular-weight substances across the cell membrane and by ingestion of solid particles. By the latter means, species of *Ochromonas* can grow in complete darkness. The relative importance of alternative types of nutrition under natural conditions is unknown. Other than for selected Chrysophyceae, few critical studies have been made on the nutritional requirements and capabilities of golden algae, because we have not yet been able to culture most of these organisms. This group offers some basic problems relating to growth, enzyme induction, and the relationship between heterotrophic and autotrophic modes of existence.

DIATOMS

Diatoms (Bacillariophyceae) resemble golden algae in the possession of both chlorophyll *a* and fucoxanthin. In addition, diatoms have a third pigment, chlorophyll *c*, which participates in photosynthesis. Excess photosynthate is stored as oil droplets in the cell cytoplasm.

There is little resemblance in form between vegetative cells of diatoms and those of golden algae. Cells of diatoms consist of two overlapping and often highly sculptured halves reminiscent of the top and bottom of a pillbox (Fig. 8-2b). Vegetative cells are nonflagellated;

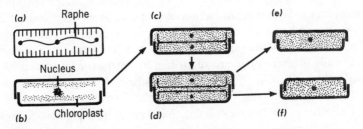

Fig. 8-2. (*a*) *Top view of a diatom cell.* (*b*) *Side view.* (*c–f*) *Stages in division.*

the only known flagellated cells are the sperm of a few marine diatoms. Shape of the vegetative cell is either radially or bilaterally symmetrical.

Perhaps the most striking characteristic of diatoms is the presence of a silicified cell wall. Silica (the basic constituent of glass, sand,

and granitic rocks) is associated with pectic substances, but the spatial relationship between these two wall components is not yet known. Utilization of silica by diatoms and other chrysophytes offers some unique biological problems. Silica compounds are relatively insoluble and are normally present in water in very low concentrations. Diatoms absorb these compounds and deposit them in the cell wall. They even absorb and hold silica against a concentration gradient. Deposition of silica in the wall is a continuous process throughout the life of the cell. It occurs in light and dark, in rapidly dividing cells, and in cells in which divisions have been inhibited experimentally. Although there have been a few reports of silica-free cells appearing spontaneously in cultures, there is no evidence that these cells are capable of continued growth and cell division. (Silica-free cells are nearly spherical in shape and appear to lack striations and other definitive markings present on normal cells.) Unfortunately, the role of silica in cellular metabolism and the importance of the silica cell wall are still unknown.

When the cell dies, silica in the wall immediately begins to dissolve. However, where conditions are especially favorable, extensive accumulations of silica walls occur. Deposits of fossil marine diatoms over 1,200 feet thick are known. Because the silica walls are very hard and inert chemically, these deposits of fossil diatoms, called *diatomaceous earth*, are mined for industrial use. Diatomaceous earth is used in insulation, as a filtering agent, and as an abrasive.

The presence of two overlapping halves in the cell wall results in a unique type of cell division. After the nucleus divides, the cytoplasm separates into two roughly equal halves. As indicated in Fig. 8-2c–f, the cytoplasm of each daughter cell then deposits a new half of a cell wall. Subsequent enlargement of the daughter cells pushes apart the overlapping halves of the original cell and, in unicellular diatoms, the daughter cells become free. Each daughter cell has half the original cell wall and has synthesized the other half of the two-piece wall. The new wall piece always forms within the old one.

Some vegetative cells of bottom-living, epiphytic, and planktonic diatoms are capable of movement even though they are nonflagellated. These forms have a longitudinal striation, called a *raphe*, on the surface of the cell (Fig. 8-2a). The raphe is a fissure in the wall through which the cytoplasm may come in contact with the substrate. It has been suggested that cytoplasmic streaming through the raphe results in the movement seen in these diatoms. Experimental evidence to support this suggestion is conflicting, and more research is needed.

SUMMARY

Group	Photosynthetic pigments	Flagella	Food reserve
Yellow-green algae	Chlorophyll *a*	One tinsel and one whiplash of unequal length	Chrysolaminarin; oils
Golden algae	Chlorophyll *a* Fucoxanthin	Mostly one tinsel, or one tinsel and one whiplash	Chrysolaminarin; oils
Diatoms	Chlorophyll *a* Chlorophyll *c* Fucoxanthin	Mostly nonflagellated	Chrysolaminarin; oils

Additional: eucaryotic cellular structure; basically unicellular or colonial; silica often present in cell wall or in wall of reproductive structure.

RELATIONSHIPS

The degree of relationship between the three groups of chrysophytes is not clear. Yellow-green algae resemble golden algae in both diversity of cell form and nutrition. Yellow-green algae differ, however, in that they lack the carotenoid pigment fucoxanthin and, when present, their flagella are always of unequal length. Golden algae are similar to diatoms in that they possess fucoxanthin, and it has been suggested that diatoms may have been derived from one of the groups of marine golden algae that have silica in their walls. Whether chlorophyll *c* (which is present in diatoms) is always lacking in golden algae has not yet been determined with certainty, since the photosynthetic pigments of very few golden algae have been studied.

With respect to the diversity of types of flagellated cells, the Chrysophyta is most likely an unnatural group. There is a marked similarity in the form and manner of insertion of flagella in Oömycetes (a fungal group) and chrysophytes (compare Figs. 3-5b and 8-1a). For this reason it has been suggested that Oömycetes (and possibly some of the other fungi) may have been derived from Chrysophyta ancestors. Further comparative studies between organisms in these two groups are needed.

9

BROWN ALGAE

Although brown algae or Phaeophyta (phaeo = brown) are common plants of rocky seacoasts of all oceans, they have their most luxuriant development along shores of cold marine waters. Brown algae are benthic organisms which, with the exception of *Sargassum,* usually do not survive long when detached from their substrates. Although *Sargassum* is primarily a benthic plant, it continues growth and undergoes vegetative reproduction by fragmentation when detached. Large quantities accumulate in the large eddy in the Atlantic Ocean known as the Sargasso Sea. Most brown algae grow in the intertidal zone where they are generally found in places exposed to the full force of wave action. The algae growing in the upper reaches of the intertidal zone are subjected to relatively long periods of desiccation during low tide. The presence of large amounts of moisture-retaining mucilaginous material in the cell wall normally prevents them from drying out completely. Many large brown algae, known as kelp, grow in the lower part of the intertidal zone or in deeper water. The giant kelp, such as *Macrocystis* and *Nereocystis,* often form spectacular underwater forests in deep water.

One of the earliest known uses of brown algae was for fertilizers, and they are still used for this purpose in some areas. At one time, brown algae were the major source of iodine used in "iodized salt," but iodine for this purpose presently comes from other sources. Several kelp, such as *Macrocystis* and *Laminaria* (Fig. 9-1), now have considerable economic importance because of colloidal compounds called alginates in their cell walls. Alginates have been used as stabilizers in ice cream, sherbet, cream cheese, and whipping cream, and as fillers in candy bars and salad dressing. They have also been used in adhesives, plastics, underwater paint, and waterproof cloth.

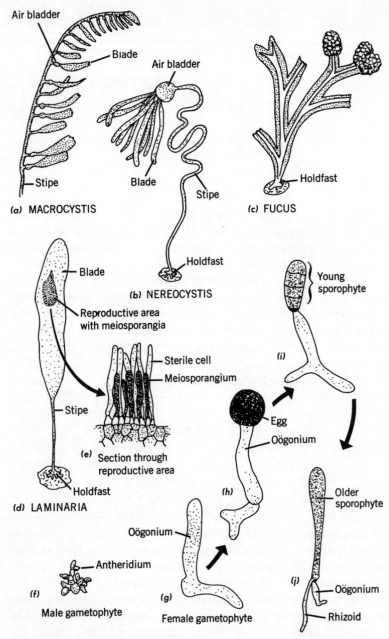

Fig. 9-1. *Brown algae. (a) Portion of the plant of Macrocystis (a giant kelp). (b) Nereocystis (a kelp). (c) Habit sketch of the rockweed Fucus. (d) Diploid plant of Laminaria (a kelp). (e) Section of the reproductive area of Laminaria blade, showing meiosporangia. (f–j) Haploid plants and early development of the diploid plant of a kelp; (f) to (i) are drawn to the same scale.*

GENERAL CHARACTERISTICS

Brown algae have a eucaryotic cellular structure. They possess chlorophyll *a* and *c* and the carotenoid pigment fucoxanthin. Several chloroplasts are generally present in each cell, and excess photosynthate is stored as the soluble sugar laminarin, a glucose polymer. The cell cytoplasm is surrounded by a wall of two layers: an inner, rigid cellulosic layer and an outer, nonrigid gelatinous layer, which may contain the alginates.

Brown algae vary from simple branched filaments with little cell specialization to giant seaweeds over 60 meters long. There are no known unicellular or colonial brown algae. Many brown algae are differentiated into basal holdfast, stemlike stipe, and photosynthetic blade (or frond); these parts functionally resemble the root, stem, and leaf of vascular plants. Some brown algae, such as *Sargassum,* also possess air floats that keep the photosynthetic parts of the plant near the water surface. Growth in size is commonly initiated by cell division in one or more localized meristematic areas. Three common genera that illustrate the morphological diversity of brown algae are described below.

Ectocarpus

Ectocarpus exemplifies the simplest type of body form in brown algae. *Ectocarpus* is a small, highly branched filamentous plant (Fig. 9-2) that grows as an epiphyte on other algae. Other than a basal holdfast and reproductive structures, there is little cell specialization. Both the type of life history and the form of the plant body are considered to be simple for brown algae as a group. *Ectocarpus* has what is termed an alternation of isomorphic generations. In other words, there is present a vegetative haploid plant during one stage of development and a vegetative diploid plant during another, and both the haploid and diploid plants are identical in vegetative morphology. The haploid (gametophytic) plant produces multicellular sexual reproductive structures called gametangia. The gametes, which are laterally biflagellated with one tinsel and one whiplash flagella, develop within the gametangia. All the gametes of *Ectocarpus* are alike in size and form and are thus termed *isogametes.*

The diploid (sporophytic) plant results from gamete fusion and zygote germination. There is no prolonged dormancy of the zygote prior to germination. The diploid plant is vegetatively similar to the

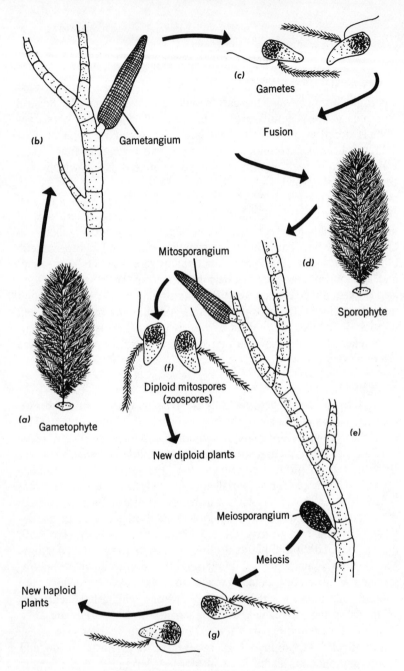

(b)

Gametangium

(c)

Gametes

Fusion

(a) Gametophyte

Mitosporangium

(d)

Sporophyte

(f)

Diploid mitospores
(zoospores)

New diploid plants

(e)

Meiosporangium

Meiosis

New haploid
plants

(g)

Fig. 9-2. *Life history of Ectocarpus.*

haploid plant and can be identified only by observation of the reproductive structures and chromosome number. Two types of reproductive structures develop on the diploid plant: mitosporangia and meiosporangia. Mitosporangia are multicellular structures and, in form, closely resemble gametangia of haploid plants. Mitosporangia produce diploid, biflagellate mitospores (zoospores) that germinate and give rise to new diploid plants. Mitospore formation and germination result in a rapid population buildup during favorable growth periods. (The haploid plant has no regular means of asexual reproduction, although unfertilized gametes often develop into new haploid plants.)

The presence of meiosporangia on the diploid plant is the only characteristic by which it is distinguished from the haploid plant. Meiosporangia are unicellular structures (and often confused with epiphytic unicellular protozoans) in which meiosis occurs. Haploid biflagellated meiospores develop within each meiosporangium. Upon germination, each meiospore gives rise to a new vegetatively haploid plant that produces gametangia.

Laminaria

The type of life history and differentiation of the plant body of *Laminaria* is characteristic of the group of brown algae known as kelp. It is a common inhabitant of the lower part of the intertidal zone. Similar to *Ectocarpus, Laminaria* has an alternation of generations. However, the two generations are dissimilar in form: they are heteromorphic. The haploid plant is microscopic and filamentous, while the diploid plant is macroscopic and parenchymatous (Fig. 9-1d–j). Because of its size and ease of collection, one thinks of the diploid plant when the name *Laminaria* is used. The diploid plant is differentiated into blade, stipe, and holdfast. The blade, which is the primary photosynthetic part of the plant, grows in length by a meristematic zone at the juncture of blade and stipe. At certain times of the year, groups of cells on the surface of the blade enlarge above the blade surface and differentiate into meiosporangia. Haploid meiospores develop within the meiosporangia. The meiospores are released and give rise to haploid plants upon germination.

There are two kinds of haploid plants: male and female. Both plants are filamentous, but the female plant is less branched and has somewhat larger cells than does the male. During sexual reproduction, a cell of the female plant develops into an oögonium. When mature, the egg is extruded from the oögonium but remains attached to the pore through which it passed. Sperm are produced in antheridia on side branches of the male plant. The biflagellate sperm swim to the nonmotile egg (by an apparent chemotactic attraction), and the fusion of sperm with egg results in the formation of the zygote. As in *Ectocarpus*, the zygote immediately germinates to give rise to a new diploid plant.

In addition to being a source of alginates, *Laminaria* is widely used as food in the Orient, especially in China. Because of its culinary importance, considerable research has been done on the ecology, development and reproduction of this plant, with the result that *Laminaria* is now cultivated in China much like a crop plant. Mature blades with meiosporangia are collected and brought into the laboratory where the gametophytes and young sporophytes are cultured. When conditions are favorable, the diploid young algae are "planted" in marine bays and allowed to grow to maturity. Seaweed culture in this manner has resulted not only in the development of a more stable economic crop, but also in the growth of *Laminaria* in areas in which it does not normally occur.

Fucus

Fucus (Fig. 9-3) is a representative of one of the most advanced brown algal groups, the rockweeds. *Fucus* and its relatives are usually the dominant organisms of the upper intertidal zone of rocky coasts. Complete desiccation during low tide is prevented by the presence of copious amounts of mucilaginous material (termed *"Fucus*-mucus" by an elementary student). As in *Laminaria,* the dominant phase of growth of *Fucus* is the diploid generation. The diploid plant is differentiated into a holdfast and a dichotomously branched axis which often contains air bladders. Growth in length of the plant is initiated by a single apical cell at the apex of each branch. Increase in diameter of the axis is initiated by the activity of a lateral meristematic zone called a *meristoderm.*

The reproductive structures of *Fucus* develop within small chambers, called conceptacles, at the swollen branch tips. According to the species, the male and female reproductive structures may be borne on the same plant (hermaphroditic condition), or on separate plants (dioecious condition). The antheridium develops on a short branch within the conceptacle. The single diploid nucleus of each undergoes meiosis to form four haploid nuclei. Each haploid nucleus then usu-

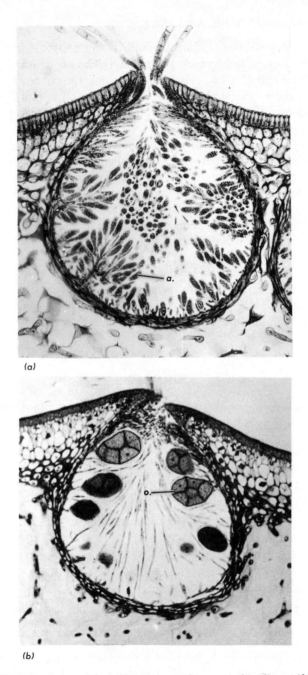

(a)

(b)

Fig. 9-3. *Fucus.* (*a*) *Male conceptacle;* a.: *antheridium.* (*b*) *Female conceptacle;* o.: *oögonium.*

ally undergoes a series of four mitotic divisions, so that a total of 64 sperm are formed within each antheridium. The oögonium develops at the distal end of a two-celled branch within the conceptacle. The diploid nucleus also undergoes meiosis, and each haploid nucleus divides once mitotically, so that a total of eight eggs develop within each oögonium.

Water loss during low tide results in shrinkage of tissues of the parent plant and detachment of the antheridia and oögonia within the conceptacles. Swelling of the mucilaginous material when wetted by the incoming tide results in the extrusion of the sperm and eggs out of the conceptacle opening into the water, where fertilization takes place. The small motile sperm are attracted to the large nonmotile egg by a chemotactic substance. Germination of the zygote occurs soon after fertilization.

Fucus differs from both *Laminaria* and *Ectocarpus* in that it lacks an alternation of multicellular generations. The vegetative phase is diploid; the haploid phase is represented only by the gametes. It is worthy of note that the life history of *Fucus* is similar to that of animals.

SUMMARY

Photosynthetic pigments	Flagella	Food reserve
Chlorophyll *a*	One tinsel and one whiplash	Laminarin
Chlorophyll *c*		
Fucoxanthin		

Additional: eucaryotic cellular structure; flagella laterally inserted; largest and vegetatively the most complex of algae; primarily marine intertidal organisms of cold water.

RELATIONSHIPS

Brown algae form a well-defined group of multicellular organisms. They resemble the chrysophytes (division Chrysophyta) in a number of respects, including flagellar form, pigmentation, and food reserve. Unfortunately, the closeness of this apparent relationship cannot yet be satisfactorily appraised. Although brown algae and diatoms possess similar pigmentation, the food reserve and the form and chemical composition of the cell wall of diatoms preclude a close (if any) relationship between these two algal groups. Golden algae and brown algae have similar flagellation, food reserve, and (except that golden algae lack chlorophyll c) pigmentation. It is curious that brown algae lack unicellular forms. This might indicate either that brown algae evolved from filamentous ancestors or that they evolved from extinct unicellular forms. A third possibility is that unicellular brown algae exist but that they have not yet been recognized. (A unicellular brown alga might be expected to have flagellation similar to brown algal mitospores, chlorophyll a and c, fucoxanthin, and store laminarin.) Perhaps future research on golden algae and other chrysophytes will help to settle this problem. The evidence now available suggests that brown algae either had a common ancestry with or were derived from the chrysophytes. If this contention is strengthened by the results of future research, there can be no justification for keeping these two algal groups (Phaeophyta and Chrysophyta) separate in a phylogenetic scheme of classification. In the future, they may be classified in the same division of the plant kingdom.

10

EUGLENOIDS

The Euglenophyta, a small, well-defined group, contains both green and nonpigmented organisms. Euglenoids are predominantly fresh-water organisms, although a few are marine. They are often abundant in places high in organic nitrogenous compounds, such as in polluted streams, wet barnyards, and margins of ponds. Although of little economic importance, they are useful research organisms.

GENERAL CHARACTERISTICS

Euglenoids are highly differentiated unicellular organisms with eucaryotic cellular structures. The cells do not possess a carbohydrate wall, but are surrounded by a modified plasma membrane called a pellicle (Fig. 10-1). Most euglenoids, such as *Euglena* and *Astasia,* have a pliable pellicle that enables the cells to change shape; the pellicle of others, such as *Phacus* (Fig. 10-1b), is rigid. The anterior end of the euglenoid cell is invaginated to form a gullet (Fig. 10-1a), which may or may not be involved in the ingestion of solid food particles. Osmotic regulation is accomplished by means of one or more contractile vacuoles present in the vicinity of the gullet. The flagellum of the euglenoids is of the tinsel type, with the lateral hair-like projections occurring in a single row on the flagellum.

Some euglenoids are photosynthetic, others nonphotosynthetic. Pigmented members contain both chlorophyll *a* and *b,* and chloroplasts may or may not possess pyrenoids. Excess photosynthate is generally stored as paramylum, a glucose polymer, which occurs as granules in the cytoplasm. However, the photosynthetic organisms are not completely autotrophic. By the use of rigorously defined media, it has been found that both pigmented and nonpigmented euglenoids are unable to synthesize vitamin B_{12}, a growth requirement. Euglenoids obtain this compound either by diffusion across the

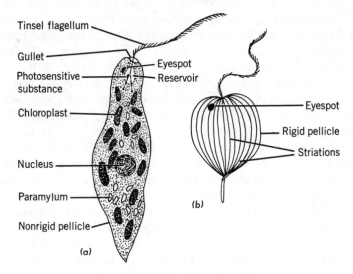

Fig. 10-1. (a) *Euglena.* (b) *Phacus.*

plasma membrane or by the ingestion of solid food particles. The growth rates of some euglenoids are so sensitive to vitamin B_{12} that they are used as assay organisms to determine unknown concentrations of this vitamin in solution.

Euglenoids undergo asexual reproduction by the longitudinal splitting of the unicell into two daughter cells. Nuclear division precedes cell division during this process. Sexual reproduction has been reported for only one genus of euglenoids. Members of the Euglenophyta survive adverse conditions by the formation of relatively thin-walled dormant cysts.

Euglena is one of the most common members of this algal division. It is also an extremely important experimental organism, from which we have obtained considerable basic information on cellular structure and function. This genus is discussed below as the specific example for this group.

Euglena (see Fig. 10-1a) is the best-known member of the Euglenophyta. It is a common organism in polluted streams, ponds, and soils of high organic nitrogen content during the warmer months of the year. It has a nonrigid pellicle, and the cell is capable of changing its shape and undergoing creeping ("euglenoid" or metabolic) movement. Although a gullet is present at the anterior end of the cell, the gullet apparently is not involved in the ingestion of solid food particles. *Euglena* is propelled through the water by means of a single tinsel flagellum. The flagellum is extended through the gullet opening. The base of the flagellum, within the reservoir of the gullet, appears to be bifid. Actually, there are two flagella present in this region, one long and one short, which are fused in the anterior part of the reservoir. Each flagellum arises from a separate basal granule within the cytoplasm. A small area that contains a photosensitive substance is present on the flagellum nearest the large, red carotenoid-containing eyespot. Experiments have shown that both the eyespot and the photosensitive substance are involved in the phototactic behavior as the organism moves through the water in a helical pattern. When swimming toward a light source, the organism's direction of motion is parallel to the light rays, and the photosensitive substance remains unshaded by the eyespot or other cytoplasmic organelles. However, when swimming in a direction other than toward a light source, the eyespot periodically darkens the photosensitive substance, which results in a change in direction of motion of the cell.

Although *Euglena* is photosynthetic, possessing several usually discoidal chloroplasts with pyrenoids, it can also be cultured in the dark for an extended period of time. When grown in the dark, *Euglena* is unable to utilize glucose as an energy source, even though glucose is a component of paramylum. On the other hand, dark-grown cultures of *Euglena* readily respire organic carbon molecules of shorter chain length such as the two-carbon acetate molecule. In this ability to utilize only short-chain carbon molecules when grown in the dark, *Euglena* resembles many algae, collectively termed *acetate* algae. This is a physiological group (containing some green algae, chrysophytes, and euglenoids) of organisms that grow in ecologically similar habitats in nature. We now know that dark-cultured *Euglena* lacks some of the phosphorylating enzymes necessary to accomplish the metabolism of glucose. The acetate molecule is readily respired in the respiratory (Kreb's) cycle.

A remarkable characteristic of several strains of the species *Euglena gracilis* is the ability to give rise to cells that are nonpigmented and thus nonphotosynthetic. Nonpigmented cells may normally appear in rapidly growing cultures of some of these strains. "Colorless" races can also be obtained by other methods—for example, by growing the cells in the dark or at elevated temperatures for an extended time period, by using radiation with ultraviolet light, or by culturing the cells in a medium containing either the antibiotic streptomycin or the antihistamine pyribenzamine. Although it is unknown whether laboratory-induced races of *Euglena* can survive in nature, a number of colorless euglenoids are known. The colorless saprobe *Astasia,* which is similar in form to *Euglena,* is of considerable theoretical interest. Because of their morphological similarity, *Euglena* and *Astasia* are referred to as a "species-pair." (Species-pairs of photosynthetic and nonphotosynthetic organisms also occur in chrysophytes, green algae, and blue-green algae.) The data above indicate that *Astasia*-like forms could have evolved from *Euglena* by the loss of chloroplasts and that they could have evolved more than once. It is well known that the antibiotic-producing Actinomycetes are common soil organisms. It is possible that antibiotics produced by Actinomycetes could inhibit chlorophyll synthesis of soil *Euglena,* which then would continue to grow as heterotrophs. Unfortunately, we have very little information about this type of interaction between soil organisms.

Because of the rapid rate of growth (short generation time) and ease of culture, *Euglena* is very useful in nutritional and biochemical research. The facility with which achlorophyllous (without chlorophyll) races are obtained increases its utility as a research organism, because it permits a study of the changes in the metabolic machinery in the transition from a photosynthetic to a completely saprobic mode of nutrition. Although chloroplasts are absent in ultraviolet light-, heat- and streptomycin-treated cells, there is evidence that chloroplast precursors, called *proplastids,* are present. (Proplastids are single-membraned vesicular structures that lack chlorophyll and photosynthetic lamellae.) Apparently because of the loss of one or more biosynthetic capacities, proplastids do not develop into mature chloroplasts. It may be significant that proplastids are present in achlorophyllous cells. It has been suggested that proplastids contain enzymes that are essential to the life of the cell but that are independent of the normal development of chloroplasts. Perhaps this theory is related to a 1962 report that chloroplasts of *Euglena* contain DNA. More recently, DNA has also been found in the chloroplasts of a few other (but not all) algae investigated, such as *Chlamydomonas* and *Acetabularia,* both green algae. The function of DNA in chloroplasts is as yet unknown, and this would seem to be a promising area of future research. It should be obvious that there is still much to learn even about classically studied structures such as chloroplasts, in *Euglena* as well as in other organisms.

SUMMARY

Photosynthetic pigments	Flagella	Food reserve
Chlorophylls *a* and *b*	One or more tinsel	Paramylum

Additional: highly differentiated cells with eucaryotic cellular structures; pellicle, gullet, and cysts.

RELATIONSHIPS

Euglenoids have a combination of characters not found in other organisms. Their food reserve (paramylum) and type of tinsel flagellum are unique. Like green plants (see Chapter 11), they possess both chlorophyll *a* and *b,* but green plants and euglenoids differ from each other in almost every other feature. Therefore the euglenoids, with no obvious relationships with other organisms, are placed in a separate division, the Euglenophyta.

11

GREEN PLANTS

Many botanists believe that embryo plants (often referred to as land plants) evolved from green algae. The reason for this belief is that green algae and embryo plants characteristically have the following in common: (1) chlorophylls *a* and *b,* (2) true starch as a food reserve, (3) starch found *within* the plastids, (4) one or more whiplash flagella (when flagellated stages are present), and (5) cellulosic cell walls. Because of these similarities, green algae and embryo plants are here placed in the same division, the division Chlorophyta (chloro = green). Thus constituted, the division Chlorophyta includes the green algae, bryophytes, ferns and fern allies, gymnosperms, and flowering plants. From man's point of view this is the most important plant division because of the economic importance of gymnosperms and flowering plants.

The division Chlorophyta is subdivided into two major groups, the subdivision Chlorophycophytina (chloro = green, phyco = algal) and the subdivision Embryophytina (embryo-producing plants). Because the coverage of this book is restricted to nonvascular plants, only the green algae and the bryophytes of the subdivision Embryophyta will be discussed here.

GREEN ALGAL PLANTS

Green algae (Chlorophycophytina) and other green plants have a eucaryotic cellular structure. Although the cell is usually surrounded by a cellulosic wall, a few flagellated, unicellular species lack a carbohydrate wall. In common with embryo plants, green algae are characteristically autotrophic organisms. Most synthesize all their needed organic compounds, including vitamins, from inorganic substrates. A few green algae lack chlorophyll and lead a heterotrophic existence. Heterotrophic green algae are considered to have been derived from autotrophic species by the loss of chlorophyll and associated biosynthetic mechanisms. Achlorophyllous green algae form species-pairs with photosynthetic species (such as *Chlamydomonas* and the nonphotosynthetic *Polytoma*). No known green algae, photosynthetic or otherwise, ingest solid food particles (as do some chrysophytes and euglenoids).

Green algae form one of the largest algal groups. They are found in a wide variety of habitats, including the surface of snow (*Chlamydomonas nivalis*) and tree trunks (*Pleurococcus*). *Pleurococcus* commonly forms green patches on tree trunks and is of interest because its unmodified vegetative cells are capable of surviving rapid temperature fluctuations as well as frequent periods of desiccation. Some green algae are components of lichens, and some live in the bodies of protozoa and *Hydra*. Most green algae are aquatic and are common organisms in fresh and marine waters. Although fresh-water species are more abundant and exhibit greater morphological diversity, marine green algae are often of greater size.

There appears to be a correlation between kind of environment (marine or fresh-water) and types of life history of green algae. Most marine green algae either have a well-defined alternation of generations (isomorphic or heteromorphic) or are vegetatively diploid. In the latter algae, as in *Fucus,* gametes are the only haploid cells present. Very few marine green algae have dormant stages in their development, a condition that may be related to their ecology. The ocean affords a relatively stable environment for the year-round growth and development of algae.

Fresh-water green algae, on the other hand, almost without exception do not possess an alternation of multicellular generations. In these algae, the haploid, gamete-producing generation (gametophyte) is the vegetative plant. The diploid stage—the result of sexual reproduction—consists of a single cell, the zygote. The zygote, in turn, soon develops a wall about itself and forms a dormant, resistant structure. Lakes, swamps, ephemeral pools and puddles, high mountain streams, large rivers, snow, soil, and trees are some habitats of fresh-water green algae. Most of these algae exhibit seasonal growth periods determined by the physical factors of the environment. Ephemeral pools soon dry up, and many fresh-water bodies are subjected to wide temperature fluctuations, changes in acidity and alkalinity, and mineral ion depletion. The advent of conditions unfavorable for vegetative growth, such as nutrient depletion, causes changes in cellular metabolism, so that sexual reproductive structures are formed with the formation of gametes. In turn, sexual reproduction leads to the development of the dormant stage—the zygospore—through which most fresh-water algae survive unfavorable growth periods.

Formation of a dormant stage is a noteworthy process because it is not an essential consequence of sexual reproduction itself. It is not a characteristic of sexually reproducing marine green algae. Zygospore formation appears to be a specific adaptation to life in the fresh-water environment.

Although the zygospore is essential for survival of many species of fresh-water green algae, others have additional means by which to survive unfavorable conditions. Some produce thick-walled asexual spores. Upon germination, these spores give rise to new haploid plants. Relatively few survive adverse periods by unmodified vegetative cells.

Practically all algal body types occur in green algae. Unicellular and colonial forms, either flagellated or nonflagellated, are found. Branched and unbranched filamentous species are common. Some filamentous species have a single nucleus per cell (uninucleate); others are multinucleate. A few green algae—mostly marine plants—are parenchymatous. Others consist of multinucleate tubes; cross walls form only in association with reproductive structures. The amoeboid cell is the only body type not found in green algae. (Even forms that lack a carbohydrate cell wall possess a definite cell shape.)

For a thorough representation of the range in morphological diversity of green algae and a pertinent discussion of algae and fungi, the student should refer to G. M. Smith's books *The Fresh-Water Algae of the United States* and *Cryptogamic Botany* (see Suggestions for Further Reading). Only a few examples of green algae will be given here.

Chlamydomonas

Chlamydomonas, a motile unicellular organism, is one of the most common green algae in nature and one often studied in elementary biology courses. Present-day representatives are generally considered to have changed little from the first evolved green algae. That is, *Chlamydomonas* is thought to represent a primitive green algal type. A study of this organism should yield insight into the basic cellular form and function of plants in this algal group. (However, it should be kept in mind that no living organisms are primitive. We cannot say that *Chlamydomonas* is a primitive alga. It is possible only to identify organisms that we assume have changed least from the original, primitive type. Thus we believe that in many respects *Chlamydomonas* has changed little from ancestral green algal stock.)

Chlamydomonas has a relatively simple cellular structure (Fig.

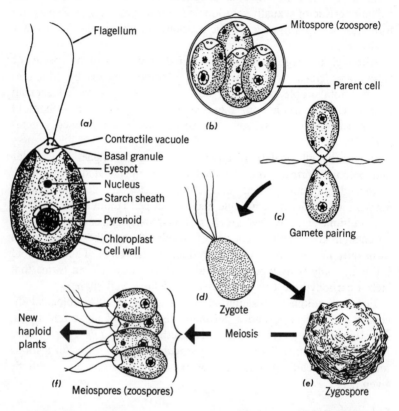

Fig. 11-1. *Chlamydomonas.* (*a*) *Vegetative cell.* (*b*) *Mitospore formation.* (*c–f*) *Stages in sexual reproduction and zygote germination.*

11-1a). Motility is provided for by two anteriorly inserted whiplash flagella. Two contractile vacuoles occur near the bases of the flagella in the cytoplasm. The large, usually cup-shaped chloroplast is the most conspicuous cellular structure. One or more pyrenoids, associated with starch synthesis, occur in the basal part of the chloroplast. The anterior part of the chloroplast usually possesses an orange, carotenoid-containing eyespot. The eyespot, a modified portion of the chloroplast, is composed of two rows of tightly packed bodies, hexagonal in section as seen with the electron microscope. The involvement of the eyespot in phototropic behavior in this organism is not yet well understood. Suspended in cytoplasm in the center of the cell, the nucleus is difficult to observe in the living cell because it is obscured by the surrounding chloroplast. A carbohydrate wall is present exterior to the cell membrane.

Although of apparent structural simplicity, *Chlamydomonas* is functionally complex. This single-celled organism has all the metabolic machinery necessary for photosynthesis, growth, and reproduction. Because of its small size, rapid growth rate, and minimal cultural requirements (only carbon dioxide, water, light, and a few inorganic ions are needed for growth), *Chlamydomonas* is a very useful research organism. Within recent years, it has been used to advantage in physiological, genetic (for studies on both chromosomal and nonchromosomal systems), and biochemical genetic research.

The developmental cycle of *Chlamydomonas* is quite simple. The young cell enlarges to a certain size, depending on the species, and divides to form new cells. During asexual reproduction, the nucleus usually divides twice mitotically, and the cell divides to form four separate protoplasts within the parent cell (see Fig. 11-1b). Each cell then secretes a wall about itself and develops flagella. Daughter cells are released into the medium when the parent cell wall ruptures. Formed as a result of mitotic divisions, the flagellated daughter cells are called mitospores (zoospores). Except in size, each mitospore is identical to the parent cell. Mitospores subsequently enlarge to mature size, at which time asexual reproduction again occurs.

Under appropriate environmental stimuli, cells of *Chlamydomonas* become nonmotile, forming the so-called *palmelloid* stage. Usually the cells in this stage are nonflagellated. Flagella reappear and the cells swim away when favorable conditions return. It is evident that the ability to lose or withdraw and to re-form or re-exert flagella, depending on environmental circumstances, is inherent in normally flagellated cells. The capacity to develop flagella is also present in many vegetatively nonflagellated unicellular and multicellular organisms—as, for example, in the formation of flagellated asexual and sexual reproductive cells by nonflagellated vegetative cells.

The process of sexual reproduction in *Chlamydomonas* lends itself well to experimental and observational study. Isogamy, anisogamy, and oögamy have been described in species of *Chlamydomonas,* but practically all research has been done on isogamous species. Most of these studies, in turn, have been made on heterothallic organisms, because the two mating types (plus and minus strains) can be separately cultured. Depletion or inadequate amounts of specific cell metabolites cause the change from vegetative growth to sexual reproduction. Either the vegetative cells themselves are directly transformed into gametes, or gametes are formed by mitotic divisions. There is no morphological difference between gametes and vegetative cells in isogamous species of *Chlamydomonas.* Under suitable conditions, moreover, gametes that do not pair and fuse may divide and give rise to new cell populations. This event indicates that there is not a great physiological difference between mitospores and gametes in this organism.

When gametes of opposite mating types are mixed together in a drop of water, there is a clumping of gametes into one or more masses. In some species, the clumping response is apparently due to attraction of gametes to substances that diffuse from gamete flagella. Flagella also play an important role in the initiation of gamete pairing. Chance flagellar contact of actively motile gametes of opposite mating types, brought into close proximity by the clumping phenomenon, results in the sticking together of the flagella (see Fig. 11-1c). The importance to sexual reproduction of flagellar sticking has been shown by experimental means. Ultraviolet-induced mutants of *Chlamydomonas* that lack flagella do not undergo sexual reproduction; they are completely asexual.

In most cases, fusion of gamete cells occurs soon after flagellar cohesion. Upon completion of cell fusion, the flagella become free and the zygote often swims about as a quadriflagellate cell (see Fig. 11-1d). The period of motility may last for a few minutes or for several weeks, depending on species and environmental conditions. Quadriflagellate zygotes of *Chlamydomonas* are similar to, and have been confused with, adult cells of the quadriflagellate green alga *Carteria.* Ultimately, the zygote loses its flagella, secretes a thick wall, and becomes dormant. Meiosis occurs during the early stages of zygospore germination and (usually) four haploid, flagellated meiospores (zoospores) emerge through the ruptured wall (see Fig. 11-1e,f).

The general process of sexual reproduction in *Chlamydomonas* is similar to that of isogamous and anisogamous green algae in general.

That is, gamete pairing is initiated by flagellar cohesion and is followed by gamete fusion. On the other hand, mating in oögamous green algae follows a slightly different sequence because the non-motile female gamete (egg) lacks flagella. In this case, the small flagellated male gamete is attracted to the egg by as yet unidentified hormonal compounds. Subsequent steps in sexual reproduction—gamete cell fusion followed by nuclear fusion—are similar.

It was previously mentioned that *Chlamydomonas* is generally believed to resemble a primitive type of green alga. This belief is supported by the relative structural simplicity of this alga (in comparison with other green algae), the simple developmental cycle, and the fact that adult cells, mitospores, meiospores, and gametes are similar morphologically.

Ulothrix

Ulothrix (Fig. 11-2), a genus of unbranched filamentous organisms, is of considerable theoretical interest. In comparison to *Chlamydomonas,* it shows (1) a differentiation of vegetative cells versus gametes, such as the development of flagellated reproductive cells from nonflagellated vegetative cells, and (2) a simple type of division of labor among cells of the filament.

Most species of *Ulothrix* are fresh-water algae, found in streams, ponds, and lakes. In Lake Michigan, *Ulothrix zonata,* a species with broad cells, grows attached to rocks at or just below the water level, with the result that many of the filaments are exposed to air during low tide. (Lake Michigan is a large enough body of water to be subjected to tidal pull to a small extent.) Periodic exposure to the air does not harm the cells even though the filaments are exposed to unfiltered sunlight. Like a few other species, *Ulothrix zonata* is a distinctly cold-water plant, appearing in Lake Michigan in the spring, disappearing during the summer, and reappearing in the fall.

The cylindrical cells of *Ulothrix* contain a single nucleus and chloroplast per cell. The chloroplast is ring-shaped and partly or wholly encircles the protoplast. One to several pyrenoids are present, depending on the species. Filaments of *Ulothrix* are attached to the substrate when young, but older filaments may break and become free-floating. Growth in length of the filament is not restricted to a specific meristematic region, but, except for the basal cell, occurs throughout the filament. The basal cell, modified into a holdfast, is the only cell in the filament that does not divide or become involved

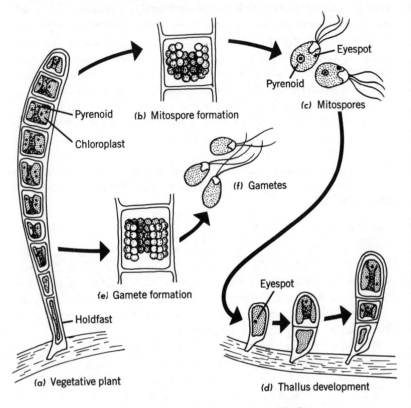

Fig. 11-2. *Stages in development of Ulothrix.*

in either sexual or asexual reproduction. Thus *Ulothrix* exhibits a very simple type of division of labor among the component cells of the filament.

The development of flagellated mitospores (zoospores) is the most important method by which a population of *Ulothrix* increases in number. During asexual reproduction, each cell of the filament, except the basal, forms one or more quadriflagellated mitospores. When more than one mitospore per cell are formed, the nucleus divides mitotically and the chloroplast and protoplast are divided up (Fig. 11-2b,c). A pore develops in the lateral wall of the cell in which they develop, and the mitospores are discharged into a gelatinous vesicle. The vesicle wall soon breaks down and the mitospores swim away. The mature mitospore has a single, cup-shaped chloroplast, an eyespot, contractile vacuoles, four whiplash flagella, and one nucleus.

Ulothrix mitospores, other than being quadriflagellate, resemble *Chlamydomonas* mitospores.

The behavior of *Ulothrix* mitospores is instructive from the point of view of the possible phylogenetic origin of *Ulothrix*. The mitospores do not have an unlimited period of motility; they ultimately settle down, flagellar end first, on a suitable substratum. Each sessile mitospore then resorbs or loses its flagella and divides repeatedly to form a uniseriate, unbranched filament (Fig. 11-2d). Several things are of interest to us here. (1) The anterior end of the mitospore develops into the holdfast cell of the mature filament. (2) The eyespot, as a result of mitotic divisions of the mitospore, ends up in the second or third basal cell of the filament. However, the eyespot, not a normal component of the vegetative cell in *Ulothrix,* soon degenerates. (Like the flagella and contractile vacuoles, the eyespot develops *de novo* during mitospore formation.) (3) The filamentous vegetative plant of *Ulothrix* develops from a flagellated cell. This sequence (development of a filamentous plant from a flagellated cell) perhaps indicates one method by which filamentous organisms evolved.

Gametes of *Ulothrix* are formed by mitotic divisions of the nucleus and cleavage of the protoplast. The mature gamete has a single chloroplast, an eyespot, contractile vacuoles, and two flagella (Fig. 11-2e,f). Except for being smaller and having only two flagella, the gametes are similar in form to mitospores. Gametes of *Ulothrix* resemble *Chlamydomonas* even more than do the mitospores. All species of *Ulothrix* are heterothallic and isogamous. Although not studied with as much precision as in *Chlamydomonas,* the details of gamete pairing and fusion appear to be similar. After gamete fusion, the diploid zygote swims about for a short time and then settles down, secretes a thick carbohydrate wall, and undergoes a rest period. Upon advent of favorable conditions, meiosis occurs and four haploid quadriflagellate meiospores emerge. Each meiospore then undergoes mitotic divisions to give rise to a new vegetative filament.

Although little experimental work has yet been done on *Ulothrix,* it appears to be a good organism for studies on factors that initiate asexual and sexual reproduction, and for studies on the resultant changes in biochemical machinery.

Enteromorpha

A discussion of *Enteromorpha* is pertinent because these organisms indicate how parenchymatous plants might have been derived from filamentous organisms. *Enteromorpha* plants also have a well-defined alternation of multicellular generations, not found in previously described green algae.

Most species of *Enteromorpha* are salt-loving, and grow in marine water as well as in inland brine lakes and salt springs. A few species are found in rivers flowing into the ocean (for example, in California). The mature plant consists of a hollow tube with a wall one cell in thickness (Fig. 11-3). Its superficial resemblance to an intestine is

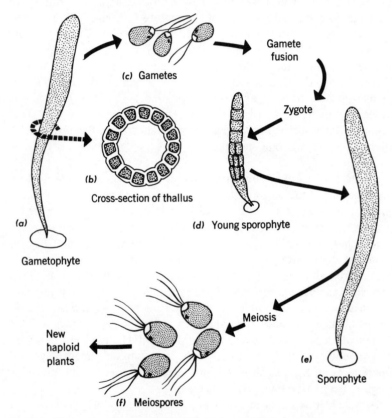

Fig. 11-3. *Stages in the life history of Enteromorpha.*

indicated by the generic name of *Enteromorpha,* literally meaning "gut-shaped." Young plants are attached to the substrate by a single basal rhizoid cell, as in *Ulothrix,* or by several rhizoidal cells. The uninucleate thallus cells each contain a single chloroplast, usually with only one pyrenoid.

During sexual reproduction, gametes may form from any cell of the haploid, gametophytic plant except the lower cells. The plants are heterothallic and gametes are isogamous in most species. Anisogamy has been reported in a few species. Following gamete fusion, the quadriflagellate zygote has a period of motility and then it settles down, retracts or loses its flagella, and forms a cell wall. The first division is mitotic and transverse to the axis of the zygote. The basal cell differentiates into a holdfast; the upper cell divides repeatedly to form a short filament. Cells of the filament then divide both transversely and vertically, resulting in the development of the parenchymatous adult plant. This is a diploid, sporophytic plant since it develops from mitotic divisions of the diploid zygote (Fig. 11-3d,e).

The sporophytic plant is identical in form to that of the haploid, gametophytic plant; thus it has an alternation of isomorphic generations. Reproduction in the diploid plant results in the formation of quadriflagellate spores. Cytological study has shown that meiosis precedes development of the flagellated cells; hence, they are meiospores. The haploid meiospores are not gametes; they do not fuse. After a short period of motility, they settle down on a substrate, retract their flagella, and undergo mitotic divisions. As in the diploid plant, a short filamentous juvenile stage precedes development of the adult parenchymatous plant. The resultant gametophytic plant ultimately forms gametes, as previously described.

During ontogeny of both haploid and diploid plants, *Enteromorpha* passes from a flagellate unicell through a filamentous plant to a parenchymatous adult organism. Thus, like *Ulothrix, Enteromorpha* is of theoretical interest. Our discussion of *Ulothrix* ontogeny indicated how filamentous organisms might have evolved from flagellated unicellular ancestors; in *Enteromorpha,* parenchymatous plants might have evolved from filamentous ones.

Gonium

Gonium is a flagellated, fresh-water colonial organism (Fig. 11-4) generally with sixteen cells per colony. Each cell has a typical *Chlamydomonas* structure: two flagella, two contractile vacuoles, a single nucleus, and one cup-shaped chloroplast with a single posterior pyrenoid and an anterior eyespot. The cells are arranged in a flat plate, surrounded by a common gelatinous matrix readily made visible by the addition of a small drop of India ink to a microscopic preparation. Individual cells are viable when the colony is fragmented, and they give rise to new colonies by asexual reproduction.

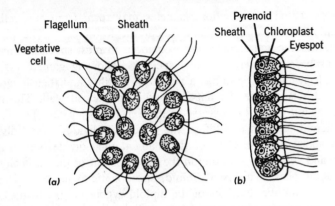

Fig. 11-4. *Gonium.* (*a*) *Surface view of colony.* (*b*) *Side view of colony.*

Cells of *Gonium* are also similar to *Chlamydomonas* cells in that they can pass through a nonflagellated palmelloid stage.

All cells of the colony are capable of asexual and sexual reproduction. During asexual reproduction, each cell of the parent colony divides repeatedly to form a sixteen-celled daughter colony. Upon breakdown of the parent colony, daughter colonies are liberated, the cells being held together by a matrix. Cells of the daughter colonies then enlarge to the adult size; no further cell divisions occur.

Gamete formation in *Gonium* resembles daughter-colony formation except that gametes are free from each other when released. Most species are heterothallic, and gamete fusion is isogamous. Details of gamete pairing and fusion are similar to those described for *Chlamydomonas.* After a period of motility, the quadriflagellate zygote retracts its flagella and secretes a wall to form a zygospore. Germination results in the formation of a four-celled colony. Each of the flagellated cells then gives rise to a new colony by means of asexual reproduction. Meiosis occurs during zygospore germination.

Gonium is the simplest member of a flagellate colonial series (volvocalean) that begins with *Gonium* and ends with *Volvox* (Fig. 5-3b). Colonies of *Volvox* may have more than a thousand cells. In this series, there is a progressive increase in cell number per colony, an increase in division of labor between potentially reproductive and wholly vegetative cells, and a change from isogamy to anisogamy and oögamy. In none of the colonial forms do vegetative cell divisions occur; colonies do not increase in cell number after daughter colonies are released from the parent colony. This is unlike the condition in *Ulothrix* and *Enteromorpha,* where vegetative cell divisions do occur. The absence of vegetative cell divisions is one reason why the so-called volvocalean line of evolution is considered to be a dead end, not leading to the development of either higher plants or animals.

Acetabularia

Some of the most elegant studies on the nuclear control of form development and on the influence of the cytoplasm on nuclear behavior have been carried out on *Acetabularia* (Fig. 11-5). These

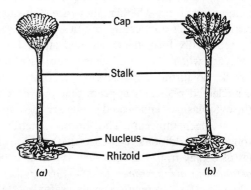

Fig. 11-5. *Acetabularia.* (*a*) *Acetabularia mediterranea.* (*b*) *A. crenulata.*

are marine organisms and can be cultured in the laboratory. The mature plant is a large single cell two to six centimeters in length and is differentiated into basal rhizoids, a chloroplast-containing stalk, and an apical cap. A single nucleus, located in one of the rhizoids, is present. Briefly, the general pattern of development is as follows. When the cap is mature, the large basal nucleus divides and numerous small daughter nuclei move in the cytoplasm throughout the plant. Resting cysts are then formed in the cap, each cyst containing several nuclei. The cysts can be induced to germinate after a period of maturation. During germination, the nuclei in the cysts divide, the cytoplasm cleaves, and biflagellate gametes develop. (Presumably, meiosis occurs during cyst formation.) The gametes fuse when released from the ruptured cyst, and the zygotes develop into new plants. This developmental cycle, which takes about one year in nature, occurs in about six months in the laboratory.

It was early found that when the cap is removed from a plant, a new cap is regenerated. *Acetabularia* is capable of regenerating missing parts. What happens when both cap and the nucleus-containing rhizoid are cut off? The experimental answer to this is that a new cap forms at the apex of the stalk. (New rhizoids seldom regenerate.) From the results of this and many other regeneration experiments, it is clear that the nucleus does not have to be present for regeneration of missing parts. Rather, regeneration appears to be under the control of cytoplasmic morphogenetic substances. The next question to be answered is whether these morphogenetic substances are, in turn, under nuclear control or whether they are self-duplicating cytoplasmic entities. If self-duplicating entities are present, then new caps should repeatedly form on enucleated stalks following cap removal. However, when the first-formed cap is removed from an enucleated stalk, no further caps develop. In contrast, caps form repeatedly in nucleated plants. It appears that the morphogenetic substances in the cytoplasm of enucleated plants are used up during formation of the first regenerate cap. The morphogenetic substances are not self-duplicating. Additional evidence that cap formation is under nuclear control comes from the following types of experiments. The stalk of *Acetabularia mediterranea* (*med*—Fig. 11-5a) is cut off just above the rhizoids. To this *med* stump is grafted a stalk (minus the cap) of *Acetabularia crenulata* (*cren*—Fig. 11-5b). In this experiment, the resultant plant essentially has a *med* nucleus and *cren* cytoplasm. It has been found that the form of the cap that regenerates at the stalk apex is always of the *med* type. In the reciprocal grafting experiment, the new cap is always of the *cren* form. From these experiments it has been concluded that the morphogenetic substances in the cytoplasm are under nuclear control and that cap formation is under indirect nuclear control.

Not only does the nucleus affect the cytoplasm, but the cytoplasm has an influence on nuclear behavior. It was previously mentioned that when the plant is mature, the nucleus divides to form numerous small nuclei. But what happens when the nucleus of a mature plant, just prior to nuclear division, is transplanted into an immature plant? Does the nucleus go ahead and divide? Results from this type of experiment are clear: the nucleus does not divide and will not divide until the cap of the plant is mature. In a similar experiment, a nucleus from a young plant was transplanted into a mature plant. Here the nucleus began to divide in about two weeks, in contrast to the two months or so that it would normally take. It has been concluded, then, that the state of the cytoplasm influences development of the nucleus.

In summary, the following interpretations of the experimental results may be made: (1) cap formation depends on morphogenetic substances stored in the cytoplasm; (2) the morphogenetic substances are under nuclear control; and (3) the state of the cytoplasm influences nuclear behavior.

Acetabularia has also proved a useful experimental organism for biochemical studies. For example, an enucleated, light-grown plant will continue growth and development for about two months. It can go through complete development up to the point of nuclear division. (Dark-grown enucleated plants quickly die.) The long-term growth of light-grown plants has led to extensive and continuing comparative studies on the physiology and biochemistry of nucleated and enucleated plants. Discussion of these investigations is beyond the scope of this book.

Spirogyra

Spirogyra is a common, filamentous fresh-water alga. It is often a conspicuous member of algal water blooms. Because of a gelatinous outer wall layer, *Spirogyra* is silky to the touch.

The most striking cellular feature, in fact the one upon which the genus is based, is the presence of one or more large helical chloroplasts in each cell (Fig. 11-6a). Each chloroplast contains numerous pyrenoids involved in starch synthesis. The bulk of the cell volume is taken up by a large central aqueous vacuole. In the center of the cell, a rather conspicuous nucleus is suspended by radiating cytoplasmic strands. Most of the cytoplasm is restricted to a thin layer surrounding the aqueous vacuole.

A definitive characteristic of *Spirogyra,* and of its relatives such as the desmids, is the complete absence of flagellated cells. In *Spirogyra,* the filament grows in length as a result of mitotic divisions and cell enlargement. Asexual reproduction occurs by fragmentation of the filament. Sexual reproduction is either homothallic or heterothallic, depending on the species. Gametic union in heterothallic forms is similar but not identical to that already described for the zygomycetous fungus *Rhizopus.* In the *Spirogyra* under discussion,

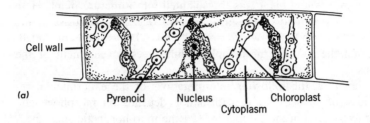

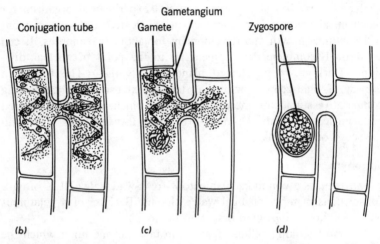

Fig. 11-6. *Spirogyra.* (*a*) *Vegetative cell.* (*b*) *Stages in sexual reproduction.*

the lateral cell walls of nearby filaments of opposite mating types bulge out slightly toward each other and then grow together. The portion of the wall in contact is dissolved to form a conjugation tube through which one of the gametes passes (Fig. 11-6b). Gametes of both mating types are uninucleate and nonflagellated, and are similar in form (isogametes). The gamete that moves is often called a "male" gamete; the stationary gamete is the "female." Fusion of gamete protoplasts and nuclei occurs in the cell (gametangium) of the female gamete. This process of fertilization is referred to as *conjugation*. The zygote immediately develops a thick wall and passes into the dormant zygospore stage. As in *Chlamydomonas,* meiosis occurs during germination, but in *Spirogyra* only a single haploid cell grows out. Three of the meiotically produced haploid nuclei degenerate prior to wall rupture; only a single haploid nucleus is functional.

Similar to *Chlamydomonas, Spirogyra* has a haploid vegetative growth phase and a diploid, single-celled dormant stage. The general patterns of life history of these two organisms are alike. Only details are different. For example, the coming together of nonflagellated gametes of *Spirogyra* is provided for through the development of a conjugation tube. There is evidence, however, that *Spirogyra* evolved from an ancestor that had flagellated male gametes. This is indicated by the presence of contractile vacuoles in the "male" gamete during its movement to the "female" gametangium. The "female" or stationary gamete lacks contractile vacuoles.

SUMMARY OF GREEN ALGAE

Photosynthetic pigments	Flagella	Food reserve
Chlorophyll *a*	Generally 2 (or more)	True starch
Chlorophyll *b*	Whiplash	

Additional: eucaryotic cellular structure; cellulosic cell wall; unicellular reproductive structures.

MOSSES, LIVERWORTS, AND HORNWORTS

The supraclasses Bryophyta and Tracheophyta are the two groups of the subdivision Embryophytina. Usually organisms in this subdivision are collectively referred to as land plants. A lignified water-conducting tissue, lacking in bryophytes, is a characteristic of tracheophytes. On the other hand, bryophytes and tracheophytes have several attributes in common—characteristics that are apparently adaptations to terrestrial life.

Embryophytes have an alternation of heteromorphic generations. In bryophytes, the gametophytic generation is long-lived and the sporophytic generation relatively short-lived; this relationship is reversed in tracheophytes. In many respects, the sporophytic plant of both bryophytes and tracheophytes shows more complete adaptation to land than does the haploid generation.

If not controlled, excess water loss by land plants—not a problem in aquatic organisms—may result in their death. However, in land plants, water loss is modified by the presence of a cuticle on the outer surface of the plant. The cuticle contains waxy substances that are impervious to water. The presence of the cuticle is characteristic of the sporophyte, not of the gametophyte.

The presence of a cuticle not only cuts down on water loss but also decreases the rate of gas exchange between the photosynthetic tissue of the plant and the atmosphere. Gas exchange in most land plants is facilitated by pores, or stomata, through which carbon dioxide, oxygen, and water vapor diffuse. Stomata, like the cuticle, are attributes of the sporophyte, not of the gametophyte. (However, stomata-like pores occur on gametophytes of a few liverworts and hornworts.)

The development of a water-conducting system was an important adaptation to terrestrial life, because it meant that not all tissues had to be in contact with water. Plants could grow up into the air; only one part, their base, had to be in an aqueous environment. In theory, then, the more efficient the water-conducting system, the larger the plants. In tracheophytes, where sporophytes are long-lived and usually of large size, the conducting systems are well developed and have lignified cell walls. Almost without exception, the small, relatively short-lived gametophytes of vascular plants lack specialized water-conducting tissue. On the other hand, the relatively long-lived gametophytes of some bryophytes have a water-conducting system, but it is not lignified. A few bryophyte sporophytes also have nonlignified water-conducting tissue. However, the whole question of the presence, distribution, and localization of lignin in bryophytes needs critical restudy. For example, lignin has been found in one liverwort (*Jungermannia*) and two mosses (*Sphagnum* and *Polytrichum*), although in no case was it associated with a water-conducting tissue. Moreover, it has been found experimentally that bryophytes, which do not normally synthesize lignin, can form lignin from eugenol (a lignin precursor). The lignin formed is quite similar to that obtained from flowering plants. Thus, at least some of the enzymes necessary for lignin formation are present in many bryophytes.

Occurrence of multicellular gametangia is another attribute of land plants. Both male gametangium (antheridium) and female gametangium (archegonium) have a sterile jacket of cells, apparently a means to prevent developing gametes from drying out. Sexual fusion in embryophytes is oögamous and occurs within specialized tissue of the female reproductive structure. Subsequent zygote germination and embryonic development of the sporophyte occur within the protective confines of the female reproductive structure. Retention of the embryo within maternal tissue is a definitive attribute of organisms placed in the subdivision Embryophyta.

General Characteristics

Bryophytes or Bryophyta (bryon = moss) are abundant in, but not restricted to, moist places. Although they grow in both arctic and arid regions, they have their most luxuriant development in tropical climates. They are common soil organisms and epiphytes (organisms that live upon other living plants). Bryophytes also grow on fallen logs and unweathered rocks, at entrances to caves, and on roofs and sides of buildings. Even though bryophytes are land plants, a few are secondarily aquatic in fresh water. None, however, live in the sea.

Individual species of bryophytes differ considerably in the range of conditions under which they can grow. Species of wide distribution usually grow in a wide variety of habitats. Other species are restricted to specific and often unusual habitats. Plants restricted to specific ecological niches often make good indicator species. For example, bryophytes in Canadian forests have been used as indicators of humidity and soil quality. One group of bryophytes, known as copper mosses, characteristically occurs only on heavy metal deposits such as copper and antimony. Some occur only on dung. Most bryophytes of restricted distribution in nature can be cultured on simple inorganic media in the laboratory. Thus bryophytes of odd habitats do not necessarily have fastidious nutritional requirements, but, unlike other plants, they can tolerate these conditions.

Bryophytes have little direct economic importance to man, with the exception of *Sphagnum,* a moss that grows in bogs. In such bogs, a combination of acidic conditions and low oxygen availability decreases the rate of bacterial and fungal decomposition of organic matter, resulting in the accumulation of extensive deposits of *Sphagnum*. These compacted and partially decomposed accumulations are known as *peat;* hence the name of peat moss for this bryophyte. Deposits are mined and used as fuel in some countries, although *Sphagnum* is not now as widely used as formerly. Because of its tremendous water-absorbent qualities, *Sphagnum* is also used as a soil conditioner. During World War I, *Sphagnum* was used as a wound dressing.

Other bryophytes are of some indirect economic importance to man. Many are "pioneer" organisms—they are among the first plants to colonize rocks, tree trunks, and disturbed soil. They, in turn, modify the environment so that other organisms are able to grow in these places. Pioneer plants are gradually replaced by other plants. Soil bryophytes, especially where they form large mats or grow on otherwise bare soil, aid in soil stabilization and decrease water runoff after rain.

There are three groups of bryophytes: hornworts, liverworts, and mosses. They all possess an alternation of generations in which a multicellular, long-lived gametophytic generation alternates with a multicellular, short-lived sporophytic generation, and in which the sporophytic plant remains permanently attached to the gametophyte. The general type of life history is one of the few important things that organisms in these groups have in common, and the relationship of these groups to each other is not yet clear.

Perhaps the manner of sporophyte growth is the best single attribute by which to separate hornworts, liverworts, and mosses. The hornwort sporophyte is an erect structure differentiated into a capsule region and a basal foot, embedded within the gametophytic plant (Fig. 11-7a). A zone of actively dividing cells—a meristem—occurs in the region between foot and capsule. As a result of meristematic activity, the capsule increases continually in length; potentially the

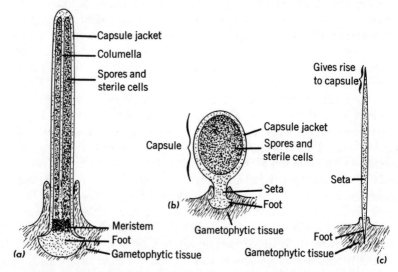

Fig. 11-7. *Form and growth characteristics of bryophyte sporophytes. (a) Hornwort, intercalary meristem. (b) Liverwort, no localized meristem. (c) Moss, apical growth.*

sporophyte is capable of unlimited growth. In nature, however, this potentiality is never realized.

The liverwort sporophyte, differentiated into capsule, seta, and foot (Fig. 11-7b), does not have a localized region of meristematic activity. For a period of time, cell divisions occur throughout the developing sporophyte, and then cell divisions cease and sporophyte maturation occurs. Sporophytic growth, apparently under precise genetic control, is decidedly limited in extent.

The mature moss sporophyte, also differentiated into capsule, seta, and foot, exhibits apical growth during development. Cell divisions at the basal end of the young sporophyte result in penetration of the foot into gametophytic tissue. Cell divisions and cell enlargement at the other end result in growth of the sporophyte into the air. The young sporophyte is spindle-shaped (Fig. 11-7c). Theoretically, the moss sporophyte should be capable of indeterminate growth; however, such growth never occurs.

The form of the bryophyte gametophyte is variable. The hornwort gametophyte is a dorsiventral, thalloid plant anchored to the substrate by means of colorless, unicellular rhizoids (rhizoid = rootlike; see Fig. 11-8a). Stomata-like pores, which lead into mucilage-filled chambers, are found on the ventral surface of the thallus in many species. Colonies of blue-green algae (occasionally nitrogen fixers) are often present in these chambers (Fig. 11-8a, c). Each cell of the thallus generally has a single chloroplast with a pyrenoid. This is the only group of embryophytes in which pyrenoids occur, and their presence is considered to be of phylogenetic significance. The gametophyte of most hornworts has no special means to survive conditions unfavorable for vegetative growth. However, a few species form *tubers*—parenchymatous structures full of reserve food.

Gametophytes of liverworts may be either thalloid or leafy (Fig. 11-9). The terms *leaf* and *stem* are here used in a functional sense. That is, the stem is the main axis of the plant and it bears or supports lateral, photosynthetic appendages, or leaves. It should be noted, however, that stems and leaves of bryophytes are not strictly comparable to those of vascular plants. In bryophytes, they belong to the gametophytic (haploid) generation; they are sporophytic (diploid) structures in vascular plants.

As in hornworts, the liverwort gametophyte is attached to the substrate by means of unicellular rhizoids. Cells of the plant possess several discoidal chloroplasts, without pyrenoids. A few species form

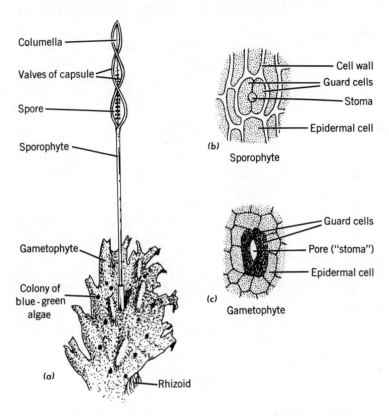

Fig. 11-8. (*a*) *Hornwort gametophyte with attached sporophyte.* (*b*) *Stoma of sporophyte of the hornwort Phaeoceros.* (*c*) *Pore of gametophyte of Phaeoceros. Note similarity in form of* (*b*) *and* (*c*).

tubers. The nature and biosynthesis of tuber food reserve and the factors that control tuber initiation need definitive study in liverworts and hornworts.

Thalloid liverworts are usually soil organisms. The dorsiventral thallus exhibits a characteristic (dichotomous) branching pattern. Plants such as *Marchantia* may exhibit considerable internal differentiation (Fig. 11-10). Note air pores (functional counterparts of stomata), air chambers, photosynthetic filaments, food-storage tissue (the cells of which lack chloroplasts), scales, and rhizoids. *Marchantia* has a specialized means of vegetative reproduction through

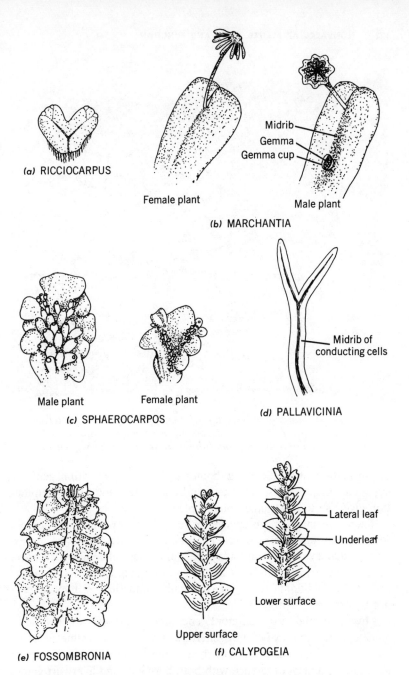

(a) RICCIOCARPUS

Female plant

Midrib
Gemma
Gemma cup

Male plant

(b) MARCHANTIA

Male plant

Female plant

(c) SPHAEROCARPOS

Midrib of
conducting cells

(d) PALLAVICINIA

Lateral leaf

Underleaf

Lower surface

Upper surface

(e) FOSSOMBRONIA

(f) CALYPOGEIA

Fig. 11-9. *Gametophytes of thalloid and leafy liverworts.*

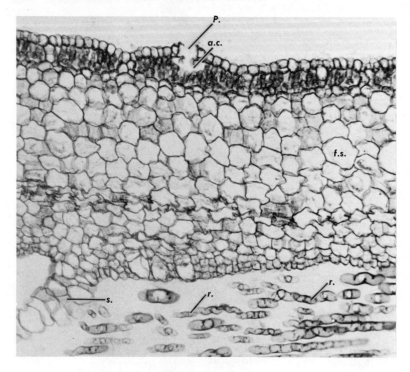

Fig. 11-10. *Marchantia. Section of gametophyte showing internal structure.* p.: *pore;* a.c.: *air chamber of photosynthetic zone;* f.s.: *nonphotosynthetic food storage zone;* s.: *scale;* r.: *rhizoid.*

the formation of multicellular bodies called *gemmae* within gemmae cups. Gemmae are dispersed by wind and water, and upon germination give rise to new gametophytic plants.

There are many more species of leafy liverworts than of thalloid forms. Leafy plants are common soil and epiphytic organisms. A few have radial symmetry and may be quite moss-like in appearance. Most, however, are dorsiventral, the stem bearing two rows of lateral leaves. An additional row of leaves, called underleaves, may or may not be present.

Mosses are the most commonly encountered bryophytes. The adult gametophytes are leafy and generally have radial symmetry (Fig. 11-11). The leafy stems are attached to the substrate by multicellular rhizoids, a point of difference with both hornwort and liverwort gametophytes. Cells of mosses possess several usually discoidal chloro-

Fig. 11-11. *Gametophyte of the moss Polytrichum grown in agar culture. Note radial symmetry and differentiation into leaf, stem, and rhizoids. Courtesy of Dr. Howard J. Arnott, Northwestern University. Reproduced by permission.*

plasts without pyrenoids. The general pattern of development of moss gametophytes and sporophytes is explored more fully below.

Mosses

Mosses often form extensive mats or carpets. They are common plants of woods, fields, and shaded stream banks. They may also be found in gardens and lawns, along paths and sidewalks, and on damp, shady sides of brick or cement edifices. Superficially they appear to form a homogeneous group, but close study shows that mosses have considerable morphological and physiological variation. The experimental potentialities of this group, and of bryophytes in general, have been largely unexploited.

It is easiest to begin a discussion of moss development with the spores. Moss spores are unicellular, haploid structures, and often have two important functions. Spores of most mosses are small and light enough to be wind-disseminated. Thus, spores may establish plants in new areas. In addition, spores of many mosses are resting structures, remaining dormant without loss of viability for variable periods of time, depending on the species. Specific factors involved in the initiation of spore germination in mosses and other bryophytes have not yet been fully elucidated. It has long been known that spores of many mosses will not germinate in the dark even though other conditions necessary for germination have been met. Light quality, minimum duration of light necessary to induce germination, and pigment system involved in the light response are areas in which further study is needed.

Spore germination results in the development of the gametophyte. Moss gametophytes, however, have two distinct growth phases: filamentous and parenchymatous. The filamentous or protonemal phase of gametophytic growth develops directly from the germinated spore. Protonema are differentiated into prostrate axial filaments with oblique cell walls and spindle-shaped chloroplasts, from which arise both rhizoidal filaments that penetrate the substrate and erect photosynthetic filaments with discoidal chloroplasts (Fig. 11-12i). This pattern of protonemal growth, called heterotrichous growth, resembles that of certain green algae. However, cells of mosses possess many chloroplasts, and chloroplasts lack pyrenoids.

After a period of protonemal growth the parenchymatous phase of gametophytic growth is initiated. Parenchymatous plants, called gametophores, arise from specialized cells that are one cell removed from a prostrate axial filament (Figs. 11-12j; 11-13a, b). This specialized initial cell then divides in different planes to give rise to an apical cell with three cutting faces. Activity of this apical cell and cell enlargement results in subsequent gametophore growth. The extent of protonemal growth prior to gametophore initiation is variable, depending on the species. In some mosses, the protonemal mat may be a few inches in diameter; in others, it may be practically nonexistent.

Gametophore initiation is a noteworthy morphogenetic phenomenon. First, only certain protonemal cells initiate gametophores. This is an excellent example of genetically identical cells exhibiting di-

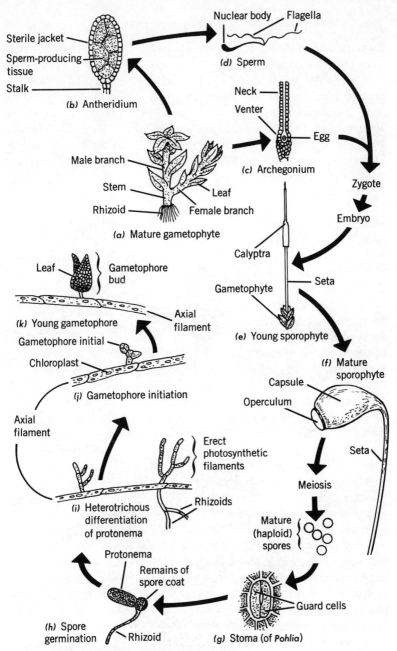

Fig. 11-12. *Illustrated life history of Funaria. (g) is from the sporophyte capsule of the moss Pohlia.*

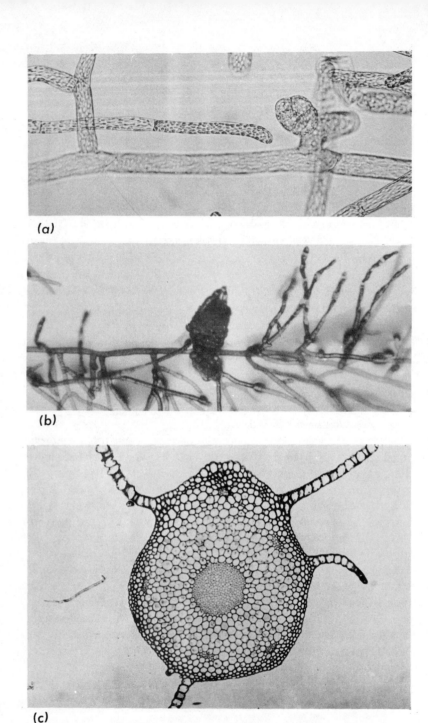

(a)

(b)

(c)

Fig. 11-13. *Top and Middle: Gametophore initiation in Funaria. Bottom: Transection of a gametophore stem of Mnium. Note central cylinder.*

vergent potentialities. Second, the timing of gametophore initiation can be altered experimentally, although gametophores of many mosses are normally initiated only after the protonemal mat has reached a certain minimum surface area. For example, light exerts considerable morphogenetic effect. Protonema cultured under very weak light intensities develop buds only when sugar (such as sucrose) is added to the medium. However, bud initiation does not occur in dark-grown cultures, even when the medium is supplemented with sucrose. It appears that in addition to providing photosynthate, light has a specific formative effect. Experiments on light quality have shown that bud initiation occurs only in cultures illuminated with red light, even though normal protonemal differentiation into axial and photosynthetic filaments occurs in both red and blue light. Thus a red-absorbing pigment is involved in gametophore initiation under these conditions. However, Polish researchers found in 1963 that the red light requirement could be replaced by the addition of kinetin (a compound that stimulates nuclear division) to the culture medium. Gametophores were initiated when this moss (*Ceratodon purpureus*) was cultured in the dark in a sucrose and kinetin-supplemented medium. It is expected that much more will be known in the next few years about the control of and changes in the biochemical pathways during gametophore initiation and development. A third thing of interest is that more than one gametophore normally develops from protonema derived from a single spore. Moreover, in most species, gametophore initiation does not inhibit further protonemal growth. Not only may a single protonemal mat give rise to a large number of gametophores; it may do so over a long period of time. This results in the formation of moss mats. Unlike gametophores, protonemal filaments do not withstand desiccation, and the advent of dry conditions brings the protonemal phase of growth to an end.

Gametophores are the mature, long-lived plants of the gametophytic phase of growth. They are the plants one identifies as moss. Although part of the gametophytic growth phase, moss gametophores superficially resemble sporophytes of vascular plants. Gametophores are differentiated into "leaves," "stems," and rhizoids. Rhizoids are multicellular filamentous structures with oblique end walls. They serve to attach the gametophores to the substrate.

There is considerable variation in the degree of complexity of the moss stem. Most stems have a central strand of elongate, presumably water-conducting cells. In many mosses (such as *Mnium*—see Fig. 11-13c) this is a simple strand of a relatively few cells. The complexity of stem anatomy of robust mosses (such as *Polytrichum*) approaches that of vascular plants. In *Polytrichum,* water-conducting, food-conducting, and strengthening elements have been identified. Lignin is lacking. However, development and relationship of form to function of moss stems has been little explored. Leaves of mosses are relatively small and usually possess a midrib, composed of elongate cells. Except in a few mosses, such as *Polytrichum,* the midrib is not continuous with the central strand of the stem.

Up to this point, our discussion has been limited to vegetative growth. The gametophore (literally, "gamete bearer") ultimately gives rise to sexual structures. Depending on the species, archegonia and antheridia develop at the apex of either the main stem or short lateral branches. Mosses are either dioecious or hermaphroditic. In some hermaphroditic mosses, archegonia and antheridia develop on the same apex; in others, such as *Funaria,* they develop on separate branches.

Antheridia and archegonia are multicellular structures and have a jacket of protective cells (see Fig. 11-12b, c). During development, the interior antheridial cells divide mitotically to produce a large number of small cells. Each nucleus, with very little cytoplasm, then develops into a sperm. During sperm development, the individual chromosomes become compacted and appressed together so that individual chromosomes cannot be discerned, and the nuclear material elongates to form the body of the sperm. Two flagella then form on the anterior end of the sperm (Fig. 11-12d). A single nonmotile egg develops in the base of the archegonium. The egg possesses a large haploid nucleus and a large amount of cytoplasm with abundant food reserve.

Water is necessary for fertilization. When water is present (even a thin film will suffice), male gametes are discharged and swim to the egg retained in the base of the archegonium. It appears that the archegonium or the egg gives off a substance that attracts sperm. Laboratory studies have shown that moss sperm are attracted to sucrose (cane sugar) but not to other tested substances. Liverwort sperm, on the other hand, are attracted to albumin (protein), not to sucrose. It is not known whether sucrose is the specific moss-sperm attractant in nature.

Gamete fusion occurs soon after the sperm comes in contact with the egg. The sperm moves across the egg plasma membrane, migrates through the cytoplasm, and comes in contact with the nucleus. Although more than one sperm may enter the egg cytoplasm (polyspermy), only one fuses with the egg nucleus. The other sperm degenerate.

Zygote germination and early sporophyte development occur surrounded by maternal tissue of the archegonium. Embryo development is usually quite rapid. The embryo foot grows down into gametophytic tissue, apparently facilitating movement of nutrients from the haploid to the young diploid plant. The other end of the embryo grows upward, stretching the confining archegonium wall, which has increased in cell number. Ultimately, the wall is ruptured, the upper part of the archegonium being carried aloft like a cap on top of the elongating sporophyte (see Fig. 11-12e). Even though broken away from the archegonium base, the cap—called a *calyptra* —undergoes a limited amount of growth and differentiation.

The calyptra is not a passive structure. It exerts considerable influence on subsequent sporophyte development, and has a very important morphogenetic effect on capsule differentiation. The young sporophyte is a needle-shaped structure. During this period of growth, cells at the calyptra tip form a tight mechanical enclosure around the sporophyte apex. As long as the calyptra is intact and pressure on the apex is maintained, the capsule does not develop. This has been indicated by results of experimental studies in which premature removal of the calyptra resulted in precocious capsule development. Capsule inhibition, at least in older sporophytes, has been shown to be due to mechanical restraint and not to hormonal control. When the calyptra is removed, the cells killed, and the calyptra replaced, no capsule develops. It is also possible to prevent capsule development by replacing the calyptra with a tight-fitting piece of tinfoil or similar pressure device. The calyptra studies mentioned above point up the need for additional research concerning the influence of both mechanical and chemical factors on sporophyte growth and capsule initiation and differentiation.

The form of the mature sporophyte is well adapted for its function, production, and discharge of spores. Capsules of most mosses are borne on top of an elongate seta. This is a distinct adaptive advantage for wind dispersal of spores. The capsule itself is usually dif-

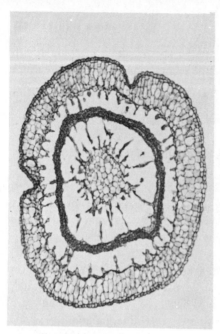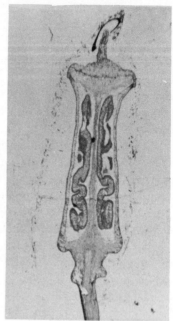

Fig. 11-14. *Sections of the capsule of the moss Polytrichum. Left: Cross section of a young capsule.   Right: Longitudinal section of a nearly mature capsule.*

ferentiated into three general regions: one region for photosynthesis, one for spore production, and one for spore dispersal. The basal part of the capsule, continuous with the seta, is specialized for photosynthesis. Stomata (see Fig. 11-12g) are present, and adjacent tissue contains abundant chloroplasts.

The central capsule region is specialized for spore formation and development. The most important feature of this region is the presence of sporogenous tissue composed of cells that undergo meiosis. The exact relationship between sporogenous tissue and surrounding nonsporogenous tissue is variable, depending on the species. One pattern is shown in Fig. 11-14 in both cross and longitudinal sections. The diploid nucleus in each cell of the sporogenous tissue undergoes meiosis to form four haploid nuclei. This re-establishes the haploid condition. A wall then forms around each nucleus and adjacent cytoplasm to form a haploid spore. Spore walls of land plants in general are impregnated with waxy compounds. These compounds are amazingly resistant to degradation, and spores—presumably of land plants —occur in the fossil record long before vegetative parts of land plants are found.

Whereas the middle portion of the capsule is involved in spore pro-

Fig. 11-15. *Peristome of Funaria. The 16 teeth, the tips of which are united, rotate in response to humidity changes.*

duction, the apical region is modified to facilitate spore discharge. A lid, or *operculum,* develops on the anterior end of the capsule (see Fig. 11-12f). When the capsule is mature, the operculum falls away. However, loss of the operculum does not usually expose the spores, because most mosses have a structure called a *peristome* (Fig. 11-15) directly under the operculum. The peristome is composed of teeth-like units, the number and form of which depend on the species. Peristome teeth generally are hygroscopic, moving in response to changes in relative humidity. In most mosses, tips of the teeth are free. In these plants (such as *Mnium*) the teeth flick out spores by bending in and out of the capsule mouth in response to changes in humidity. Peristome teeth of other mosses may be joined at the tips. In these plants, the teeth may be hygroscopic (*Funaria*) or rigid (*Polytrichum*). (It is of interest that lignin has been found in the peristome teeth of *Polytrichum.*) Spores of these plants sift out through openings between adjacent teeth. Peristome teeth function to hinder the rate of spore discharge, thus providing for dispersal over a longer period of time. However, many mosses lack peristome teeth and are as well distributed as those that have them. Wind and water are the two most important agents of spore dispersal. Spores of a few mosses, such as those of coprophilous species of *Splachnum*, are insect-disseminated.

With perhaps one exception (*Buxbaumia*), sporophytes of mosses (and other bryophytes) are permanently attached to the gametophyte. This relationship has led to a discussion of the degree of nutritional independence of the sporophyte. A few comments on this subject are pertinent here. The young moss embryo is nonphotosynthetic. Similar to embryos of plants and animals in general, moss embryos are nutritionally parasitic on surrounding tissue. However, most moss sporophytes soon develop chloroplasts and subsequently store abundant starch. Analysis has shown that sporophytes possess the same photosynthetic pigments (chlorophylls *a* and *b*) as gametophytes. Quantitatively, they may possess a higher concentration of these pigments. Although photosynthetic incorporation of radioactive carbon (in carbon dioxide) into sugars has not yet been studied, the data above are strong evidence that moss sporophytes are photosynthetic. It is obvious that moss sporophytes obtain water and minerals, and perhaps other compounds, from the gametophytes.

The form of the sporophyte contrasts sharply with that of the gametophyte. The sporophyte lacks leaves and rhizoids and does not branch. Experimental studies have shown that the characteristic form of the sporophyte is not a necessary consequence of the diploid condition. Severed from the foot and capsule and placed on a suitable medium, it is possible to induce seta cells to divide. However, cell division and differentiation do not result in development of new sporophytic parts. Instead, the diploid seta cells give rise to protonemal filaments. Cell size is somewhat larger, but otherwise the filaments are identical to those derived from haploid spores. Moreover, diploid gametophores develop from diploid protonema, and gametes produced are also diploid. Fusion of diploid gametes results in the formation of a sporophyte that is tetraploid. This is twice the number of chromosomes that are present in a normal sporophytic plant. From this type of study it is evident that the number of chromosomes in the nucleus does not explain the morphological differences between gametophytic and sporophytic generations. We must look elsewhere for an explanation of the basis of alternation of heteromorphic generations found in mosses and other embryophytes.

SUMMARY OF BRYOPHYTES

Photosynthetic pigments	Flagella	Food reserve
Chlorophyll *a*	Whiplash	True starch
Chlorophyll *b*	(sperm only)	

Additional: eucaryotic cellular structure; conducting system, when present, nonlignified; dominant gametophytic generation; cellulosic cell wall; multicellular sexual reproductive structures; primarily land plants.

RELATIONSHIPS OF CHLOROPHYTA

Many organisms have chlorophylls *a* and *b,* store food as true starch within plastids, and, when flagella are present, have flagella of the whiplash type. Plants with this combination of characteristics are placed in a separate plant group, the division Chlorophyta. The presence of similar morphological and physiological attributes indicates that chlorophytes have many similar biochemical pathways. Therefore, plants within the division Chlorophyta can be considered to be more closely related to each other than they are to plants in other divisions.

It is believed that there is a close evolutionary relationship between green algae and embryophytes and that primitive green land plants arose from early algal stock. This relationship has been acknowledged by placing embryo plants and green algae in the same plant division. Unfortunately, there is little fossil evidence to indicate the stock group of green algae from which green land plants evolved. Not only do primitive green land plants appear in the fossil record about the same time as green algae, but there are also no known intermediate fossil forms. Of course, this kind of negative datum is difficult to evaluate. Absence from the fossil record might be due to several factors. It does not necessarily mean that these organisms did not exist. Because of their relatively small size and lack of hard parts, green algae are not favorable material for fossilization.

Therefore, other kinds of evidence must be used in order to attempt to identify the most likely stock group ancestral to green land plants. In the green algal order Ulotrichales (among other genera this order includes *Ulothrix, Pleurococcus,* and *Enteromorpha*), there is great morphological diversity—the type of diversity that gives insight into how embryo plants might have evolved. Given species of ulotrichalean algae consist of unbranched or branched filaments, or of parenchyma.

Some filamentous species are highly differentiated, having a prostrate system from which arise numerous branched photosynthetic filaments and rhizoidal filaments that penetrate the substratum. In this respect, *Fritschiella* is of particular interest because not only does it possess an erect, prostrate, and rhizoidal system (the heterotrichous habit of growth), but it also grows on mud in India. *Fritschiella* is a contemporary green algal land plant. The habitat of *Pleurococcus* also is noteworthy in that it shows that ulotrichalean green algae can survive in a terrestrial environment without formation of specialized cells.

In summary, we find that ulotrichalean green algae exhibit considerable morphological diversity as a group. In addition to simple unbranched filamentous organisms, highly differentiated filamentous and parenchymatous types are found. Some are strictly aquatic organisms, while others exhibit at least partial adaptation to a land environment. For these reasons, it is believed that green land plants evolved from an early stock of ulotrichalean green algae. This concept is diagrammatically represented in Fig. 11-16. This representation is an over-

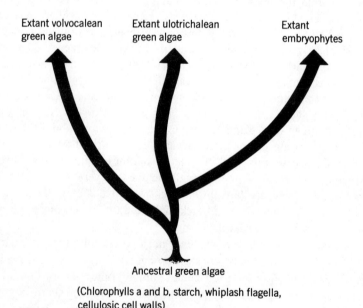

Extant volvocalean green algae

Extant ulotrichalean green algae

Extant embryophytes

Ancestral green algae

(Chlorophylls a and b, starch, whiplash flagella, cellulosic cell walls)

Fig. 11-16. *Presumed relationship between green algae and green land plants.*

simplification. However, it does graphically illustrate the belief that embryophytes are genetically related to green algae, especially ulotrichalean green algae. A discussion of the degree of relationship of bryophytes to tracheophytes and whether primitive embryophytes evolved from a single algal ancestor (monophyletic origin of land plants) or whether different groups of embryophytes evolved from different algal ancestors (polyphyletic origin) is beyond the scope of this book. Regardless of manner of origin, the tracheophytes are the most important economic group of plants to man. They are man's staff of life. On the other hand, much of man's understanding of life's processes has been, and will continue to be, obtained from studies utilizing nonvascular plants.

SUGGESTIONS FOR

FURTHER READING

Alexopoulos, C. J. *Introductory Mycology,* 2nd ed. New York: John Wiley & Sons, Inc., 1962.

Bonner, J. T. *The Cellular Slime Molds.* Princeton, N.J.: Princeton University Press, 1959.

Bopp, M. von. "Morphogenese der Laubmoose." *Biological Review,* Vol. 36 (1961), pp. 237–280.

Cantino, E. C. "Physiology and Development of Lower Fungi (Phycomycetes)." *Annual Review of Microbiology,* Vol. 13 (1959), pp. 97–124.

Christensen, C. M. *The Molds and Man,* 2nd ed. Minneapolis: University of Minnesota Press, 1961.

Emerson, R. "The Biology of Water Molds." In *Aspects of Synthesis and Order in Growth.* Princeton, N.J.: Princeton University Press, 1955, pp. 171–208.

Gibbs, S. P. "The Ultrastructure of the Chloroplasts of Algae." *Journal of Ultrastructure Research,* Vol. 7 (1962), pp. 418–435.

Gunsalus, I. C., and R. Y. Stanier, eds. *The Bacteria: A Treatise on Structure and Function.* New York: Academic Press, 1960.

Hale, M. E., Jr. *Lichen Handbook.* Washington: Smithsonian Institution, Publication 4434, 1961.

Ingold, C. T. *Dispersal in Fungi.* Oxford: Clarendon Press, 1953.

Jaffe, L. F. "Morphogenesis in Lower Plants." *Annual Review of Plant Physiology,* Vol. 9 (1958), pp. 359–384.

Krauss, R. W. "Physiology of the Fresh-Water Algae." *Annual Review of Plant Physiology,* Vol. 9 (1958), pp. 207–244.

Large, E. C. *The Advance of the Fungi.* New York: Henry Holt and Co., 1940.

Lewin, R. A., ed. *Physiology and Biochemistry of Algae.* New York: Academic Press, 1962.

Näf, U. "Developmental Physiology of Lower Archegoniates." *Annual Review of Plant Physiology,* Vol. 13 (1962), pp. 507–532.

Nickerson, W. J. "Molecular Bases of Form in Yeasts." Symposium on Biochemical Bases of Morphogenesis in Fungi, IV. *Bacteriological Reviews,* Vol. 27 (1963), pp. 305–324.

Parihar, N. S. *An Introduction to the Embryophyta: I. Bryophyta.* 4th rev. ed. Allahabad, India: Central Book Depot, 1961.

Plunkett, B. E. "The Influence of Factors of the Aeration Complex and

Light upon Fruit-Body Form in Pure Culture of an Agaric and a Polypore." *Annals of Botany,* Vol. 20 (1956), pp. 563–586.

Raper, J. R. "Hormones and Sexuality in Lower Plants." Symposia of the Society for Experimental Biology, No. 11 (1957), pp. 143–165.

Raper, J. R. "The Control of Sex in Fungi." *American Journal of Botany,* Vol. 47 (1960), pp. 794–808.

Smith, A. H. *The Mushroom Hunter's Field Guide.* Ann Arbor: University of Michigan Press, 1960.

Smith, G. M. *The Fresh-Water Algae of the United States,* 2nd ed. New York: McGraw-Hill Book Co., Inc., 1950.

Smith, G. M., ed. *Manual of Phycology.* Waltham, Mass.: Chronica Botanica, 1951.

Smith, G. M. *Cryptogamic Botany,* Vol. 1, 2nd ed. New York: McGraw-Hill Book Co., Inc., 1955.

Sparrow, F. K. *Aquatic Phycomycetes,* 2nd rev. ed. Ann Arbor: University of Michigan Press, 1960.

Verdoorn, Fr., ed. *Manual of Bryology.* The Hague: M. Nijhoff, 1932.

GLOSSARY

Acetate algae. A physiological group of algae that are unable to respire hexose sugars when cultured in the dark, but do respire short-chain carbohydrate molecules such as acetate.

Achlorophyllous. Without chlorophyll.

Alternation of generations. The alternation of a meiospore-producing, diploid growth phase with a gamete-producing, haploid growth phase in the life cycle of an organism.

Amitosis. Nuclear division without the formation of spindle fibers and distinct chromosomes.

Anisogamy. Sexual fusion in which flagellated gametes are of dissimilar size.

Antheridium. Unicellular or multicellular gametangium of plants in which sperm are produced.

Apothecium. An open, generally cup-shaped fruiting body of Ascomycetes.

Archegonium. Multicellular gametangium of plants in which an egg is produced.

Ascospore. A spore formed in an ascus.

Ascus (pl. *asci*). A sac-like structure of Ascomycetes in which nuclear fusion and meiosis occur and meiospores develop.

Autoecious. Completing its life cycle on a single host species.

Autotrophic. The ability to utilize light energy, or the energy derived from the oxidation of inorganic compounds, to drive synthetic reactions in the cell.

Axenic. Having only one kind of organism present in a culture.

Bacteriophage. A virus that infects bacteria.

Basidiospore. A spore formed on a basidium.

Basidium. A structure in Basidiomycetes in which nuclear fusion and meiosis occur and which (usually) produces four meiospores.

Benthic. Living attached at the bottom of aquatic habitats, such as ponds, lakes, or oceans.

Biliproteins. Water-soluble, accessory photosynthetic pigments of red or blue color.

Calyptra. Gametophytic tissue (derived from the upper part of the archegonium) carried aloft by and forming a covering over the apex of the developing sporophyte of a moss.

Capsule. In bryophytes, a multicellular meiospore-producing structure.

Carbohydrate. An organic molecule containing carbon, hydrogen, and oxygen; the hydrogen and oxygen are in a 2:1 ratio.

Chemoautotrophic. The ability to use energy derived from the oxidation of inorganic compounds for the synthesis of organic foods.

Chromatophores. The membrane system in procaryotic organisms in which the photosynthetic pigments are located.

Cleistothecium. A completely closed fruiting body of Ascomycetes.

Coenozygote. A multinucleate zygote resulting from the union of two multinucleate gametangia.

Coli-phage. A virus that infects *Escherichia coli*.

Conceptacle. A cavity in *Fucus* and its relatives in which gametangia develop.

Conidiophore. A specialized hypha that bears conidia.

Conidium. A nonflagellated mitospore cut off sequentially from the tip or side of a hypha.

Cuticle. A waxy coating characteristic of, but not restricted to, the epidermis of embryophyte sporophytes.

Dichotomous. Division of an axis into two equal branches.

Dikaryotic. Having paired nuclei, each usually derived from different parents.

Dimorphism. Having two different forms.

Dioecious. Sexes segregated on different plants; each plant producing only one type of sex organ.

Diploid. Having two full chromosome complements per nucleus.

Dorsiventral. Flattened with dissimilar dorsal and ventral surfaces.

Egg. A nonmotile female gamete that can fuse with a sperm.

Embryo. A multicellular young organism, developed from the zygote, which is surrounded by female reproductive tissue.

Epiphytes. Organisms that live on the surface of living plants.

Eucaryotic. Possessing a true nucleus; more generally, having double-membrane cell organelles such as nucleus, mitochondrium, and chloroplast.

Flagellum. A whip-like or tinsel-like appendage that generally serves to propel a motile cell.

Foot. In bryophytes, a specialized absorptive structure of the sporophyte, embedded in gametophytic tissue.

Fruiting body. In fungi and slime molds, any structure that contains or bears spores.

Gametangium. A unicellular or multicellular structure in which gametes are formed.

Gametophore. In mosses, the leafy structure on which antheridia and archegonia are borne.

Gametophyte. The generally haploid, gamete-producing plant.

Gemma. A vegetative reproductive body, such as in liverworts, which becomes detached and develops into a new plant.

Habitat. The particular environment where an organism is usually found.

Haploid. Having one full chromosome complement per nucleus.

Haustorium. A specialized, nutrient-absorbing cell or tissue of parasites.

Hermaphroditic. Having both male and female sex organs on one individual.

Heteroecious. Requiring two different host species in order to complete its life cycle.

Heteromorphic. Having more than one form.

Heterothallic. Requiring two different plants for sexual reproduction; may either be dioecious or hermaphroditic (but self-incompatible).

Heterotrichous. Differentiated into prostrate, rhizoidal, and erect systems.

Heterotrophic. Having energy needed to drive synthetic reactions coming from breakdown of organic compounds; organisms live as parasites or saprobes.

Holdfast. In algae, a cell or group of cells that serve to attach the organism to a substrate.

Homothallic. Having sexual reproduction on a single thallus; these plants are both hermaphroditic and self-compatible.

Hygroscopic. Sensitive to moisture.

Hypha. A fungal filament.

Isogamy. Sexual fusion in which the gametes are of similar size and form.

Isomorphic. Having one form.

Mating type. Term used for heterothallic organisms in which the sexes cannot visibly be separated.

Meiosporangium. A unicellular or multicellular structure in which meiosis occurs and in which meiospores develop.

Meiospore. Flagellated or nonflagellated reproductive cell of a plant produced following meiosis.

Meristem. Embryonic tissue of plants capable of cell divisions and giving rise to other tissues.

Mitosporangium. A structure in which mitospores develop.

Mitospore. The flagellated or nonflagellated reproductive cell of a plant produced following mitosis.

Monokaryotic. Having a single nucleus, or several nuclei of the same genetic type, in each cell.

Monophyletic. Of a single line of descent.

Morphogenesis. The development of form and structure.

Mutualism. The living together of two or more organisms in close association, in which each organism benefits from the relationship.

Mycelium. The mass of hyphae of a fungus.

Mycorrhiza. Close association between fungal hyphae and roots of vascular plants.

Ontogeny. The development of an individual.

Oögamy. Sexual fusion in which a sperm fuses with a large, nonmotile egg.

Oögonium. Unicellular gametangium in which one or more eggs develop.

Operculum. In mosses, the lid at the apex of the capsule; it usually comes off at capsule maturity.

Palmelloid. A transient nonmotile stage in the life histories of many motile algae such as *Chlamydomonas;* the cells become embedded in a gelatinous matrix.

Parasitism. A form of symbiosis in which one organism lives at the expense of the other.

Perithecium. A spherical or flask-shaped fruiting body of Ascomycetes, containing an opening.

Photoautotrophic. Capable of utilizing light energy for the synthesis of food from inorganic compounds.

Phototropism. A directional growth response toward or away from light.

Phylogeny. The historical development or evolutionary history of a group.

Plankton. Generally microscopic floating or flagellated organisms that are readily carried about by water currents.

Plasmodium. A multinucleate mass of naked protoplasm, constituting the predominant vegetative phase of slime molds.

Plastid. A double-membraned cell organelle involved in the synthesis and/or storage of food; one type is the chloroplast.

Polymer. A large molecule composed of identical or similar units; for example, starch made up of glucose units.

Polyphyletic. Having several lines of descent.

Procaryotic. Literally, before a nucleus; lacking double-membrane structures.

Proplastids. Single-membrane, vesicular cell organelles that lack chlorophyll and discs and that are capable of developing into chloroplasts.

Protonema (pl. *protonemata*). Literally, first thread; in mosses, the filamentous growth phase developing from spore germination.

Pseudopodium. Literally, a false foot; temporary cytoplasmic extension of a cell.

Pyrenoid. A specialized, proteinaceous part of the chloroplast of many algae and of hornworts, and closely associated with starch synthesis in green algae and hornworts.

Respiration. In plants, the cellular stepwise anaerobic or aerobic liberation of energy during the breakdown of organic molecules.

Rhizoid. An absorptive and anchorage structure in nonvascular plants.

Saprobe. An organism that lives on dead organic matter.

Saprotism. The condition of living on dead organic matter.

Septum (pl. *septa*). A partition or cross wall.

Seta. In mosses, the stalk that bears the sporophyte capsule.

Sperm. A usually flagellated male gamete that can fuse with an egg.

Spermagonium. The structure in which are produced spermatia of fungi such as those in rusts.

Spermatium. Name for the nonflagellated male gamete of red algae and some fungi such as rusts.

Sporangiophore. A sporangium-bearing structure.

Sporangium. A unicellular or multicellular structure in which spores are produced.

Sporogenous. Producing spores.

Sporophyte.   The meiospore-producing plant; generally diploid.

Stipe.   A stem-like structure of mushrooms or brown algae.

Stolon.   In fungi such as *Rhizopus,* a prostrate filament from which arise rhizoids and sporangiophores.

Stoma (pl. *stomata*).   A microscopic pore, surrounded by guard cells, which facilitates gas exchange between interior tissue of the plant and the atmosphere.

Symbiosis.   The relationship of two organisms living in close association with each other.

Syngamy.   The fusion of gametes.

Teliospore.   A thick-walled resting spore in rusts and smuts in which nuclear fusion occurs; gives rise to the basidium.

Tetraploid.   Having four full chromosome complements per nucleus.

Thallus.   A plant body not differentiated into leaf-like, stem-like, and root-like organs.

Uredospore.   A binucleate spore, formed in rusts, which is capable of reinfecting the same species on which the spore is formed.

Venter.   Base of the archegonium; contains the egg.

Xylem.   Lignified water-conducting tissue of tracheophytes.

Zoosporangium.   A sporangium in which flagellated mitospores (zoospores) are produced.

Zoospores.   A general term that includes both flagellated mitospores and flagellated meiospores.

Zygote.   A diploid cell formed by fusion of gametes.

INDEX